NORTHUMBRIAN
ROCKS AND
LANDSCAPE
A FIELD GUIDE

YORKSHIRE GEOLOGICAL SOCIETY

•

EDITED BY COLIN SCRUTTON

CW00553574

Ellenbank
Press

YORKSHIRE
GEOLOGICAL
SOCIETY

The objectives of the Yorkshire Geological Society are to extend the knowledge of the science of geology and to promote and record the results of geological research, with particular emphasis on the North of England.

The Society publishes a journal, the *Proceedings of the Yorkshire Geological Society*, devoted to original work on geology and geomorphology with the emphasis on northern England. A Circular is distributed about six times a year to publicise the winter programme of lectures, the summer field meetings and various other matters of interest to members.

No qualifications are required for membership and there is no entry fee. For further information on the Society and a Membership Application Form, please write to:

John Varker, General Secretary,
Department of Earth Sciences, The University,
Leeds, LS2 9JT.

Also in this series:
Lakeland Rocks and Landscape
Yorkshire Rocks and Landscape

Published by Ellenbank Press, Park Hill South,
Camp Road, Maryport, Cumbria CA15 6JN

First published 1995

Typeset in Linotron Baskerville by Deltatype Ltd,
Ellesmere Port, Cheshire
Printed and bound by St Edmundsbury Press,
Bury St Edmunds, Suffolk

British Library Cataloguing in Publication Data
A catalogue record for this book is available from
the British Library

ISBN 1 873551 11 8

Contents

Contents

*Officers of the British Geological Survey publish with the permission of the Director.

Preface

This field guide, the second to be sponsored by the Yorkshire Geological Society, is mostly written and edited by its members. The Society has a long and distinguished history, having been founded in 1837. From small beginnings among amateurs with an interest in Yorkshire geology, it has grown to have influence well beyond the boundaries of the county and a membership of over 1000 from all over the world. It brings together professional geologists of all descriptions, from universities, surveys and companies, together with amateur geologists who still form a significant proportion of our membership. The Society publishes a prestigious journal, the *Proceedings*, which has a major part of its original papers based on Yorkshire geology. The original aims of the Society are still observed in the lecture meetings held approximately monthly from October to March, and particularly in the programme of field excursions in the spring and summer months. The lectures are a mixture of original work, mainly on the geology of Yorkshire and Northern England, and general reviews often of much wider scope. Field excursions range all over the county and its near neighbours and offer an opportunity to demonstrate new observations and interpretations of the geology and geomorphology.

Many of you using this guide may already be members of the Yorkshire Geological Society. If you are not, and would like to know more about this fascinating subject, why don't you join us? We would be pleased to welcome you.

Colin Scrutton, President, Yorkshire Geological Society

Introduction

For the purposes of this book, Northumbria is defined as Northumberland, Durham, Tyne & Wear, and Cleveland north of the River Tees. The excursions described provide a broad coverage of this area and its borders, both geographically and geologically, although in a publication of this size a selection inevitably has to be made from among the wealth of excellent sites available. Wherever you live, or are staying in the area, we hope there will be something to interest you.

An introductory chapter outlines the geological history of Northumbria, providing a framework for the details of the local geology. Each excursion begins with notes on access, duration, useful Ordnance Survey (O.S.) and British Geological Survey (B.G.S.) maps, and background information on the geology and geomorphology. In many cases, observations on historical, archaeological and other related matters are included. A section towards the end of the book lists museums in Northumbria that have geological displays or collections.

All excursions have certain basic requirements for both safety and enjoyment. These include stout shoes or walking boots, sensible clothes including waterproofs in case of rain, and appropriate maps for location in the field. On higher ground, it may be much colder and more windy than in the valleys, and low cloud may not just spoil appreciation of geological and geomorphological views of the landscape, but may present a danger if you become lost. On foreshores, wellington boots may be a suitable alternative, but whatever your footwear, wet rocks can be very slippery, particularly those with veneers of green algae.

For more specific dangers, notes are given in the introductory material to appropriate excursions. However, it is worth repeating some general points. In locations near quarry or cliff faces, a safety helmet should be worn. Always look at the state of steep faces and if in doubt about their safety, do not approach them. When using a hammer, it is advisable to wear safety goggles and to make sure that fragments chipped off will not hit other people. In any coastal situation, the state of the tide may be crucial, not only to your view of the geology but to your safety as the tide comes in. Always check on the time of low tide and do not start an excursion on a rising tide where access to and from the foreshore is limited. Tide tables for the mouth of the Tyne are available from The Port of Tyne Authority, Bewick Street, Newcastle upon Tyne, NE1 5HS (tel. 232 5541), and tide times are published in local newspapers. Finally, if visiting remote locations alone, tell someone where you are going.

Some excursions include visits to Sites of Special Scientific Interest. These are designated not only to conserve our geological heritage but to protect other features, such as the flora. Please observe any particular requests not to hammer rocks or to collect fossils.

As far as possible, excursion routes follow public rights of way and keep to open land or the foreshore. However, where localities are on private land, permission for access should be sought beforehand. We have given as much information as possible to facilitate this. In general, observe the Countryside Code and avoid damage to walls, gates or property. The Geologists Association have published a Code for Geological Field Work, which outlines good practice in the field and can be obtained from the Librarian, The Geologists Association, Department of Geological Sciences, University College, Gower Street, London WC1E 6BT.

Anyone with a general interest in geology and geomorphology should be able to follow the excursions in this guide. However, the complexity of the geology and level of technical description varies from place to place. As an aid, selected technical terms are highlighted in **bold** on first usage in each section and are briefly defined in a Glossary at the end of the book. For more information on any term, or for terms not covered, reference should be made to a geological dictionary (see Bibliography). Bibliographic entries are placed towards the end of the book and are mainly general works. A few more specific references are included where these have value for a particular excursion.

Finally, I would like to thank all those who have helped me in the compilation of this guide, particularly my colleague Brian Turner, and the authors for their contributions.

Colin Scrutton, University of Durham

Note

The details of routes given in this guide do not imply a right of way. Users of this guide are responsible for seeking permission where necessary to use footpaths and for access to any private land.

Every effort has been made to ensure that the contents of this book are accurate and up-to-date. However, information on any changes to footpaths or exposures, or threats to any S.S.S.I., would be welcomed by the Society.

Notes on safety have been included but it is the responsibility of the user to take all necessary precautions for their own safety and that of third parties. The publishers and the Society take no responsibility for any accident or injury sustained on any of these excursions.

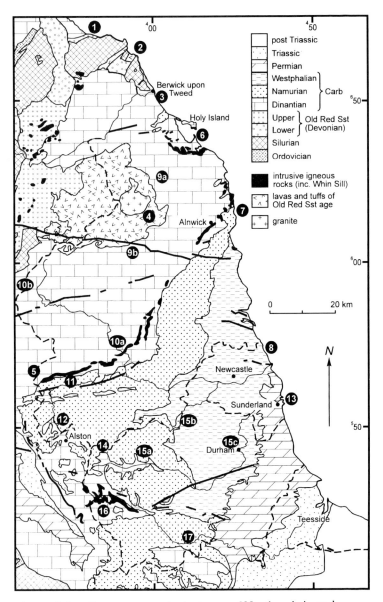

Figure 1 Pre-Quaternary geological map of Northumbria and adjoining areas showing the location of excursions.

Geological history of Northumbria

Colin Scrutton *University of Durham*

Northumbria (Northumberland, Durham, Tyne & Wear and Cleveland north of the Tees) is dominated by rocks of Carboniferous age (Figs. 1, 2). On the northern margin of the area, they rest on a range of older rocks in the Scottish borders, principally Silurian sediments and the lavas of the early Devonian Cheviot volcano. Lower Carboniferous sediments, which crop out on the coast of north Northumberland, form a broad belt inland, skirting the ancient volcanic pile and striking southwest parallel to the Scottish border, before turning south-southeast along the Pennine front. Gentle easterly and southeasterly **dips** bring in the mid Carboniferous to the southeast, forming a narrow triangular outcrop with its apex on the mid Northumberland coast and its base forming the north Pennine peaks and the Durham dales. The upper Carboniferous Coal Measures in turn form the south Northumberland coast and extend inland as a north–south outcrop, widest at the Tyne and narrowing into south Durham. There, the Coal Measures are **overstepped** by the Permian, which rests **unconformably** upon them. These Permian rocks form the high ground in the east of County Durham and the distinctive buff coastal cliffs of Durham and Tyne & Wear. They pass up into Triassic rocks underlying the low ground of Tees-side. Younger Mesozoic and Tertiary rocks, apart from some small **igneous** intrusions, are not preserved in Northumbria, but the effects of the Pleistocene glaciation are apparent everywhere. **Tills** mantle the solid rocks, particularly thickly in central and south Durham.

As well as dominating Northumbria geologically, Carboniferous rocks, with their natural resources, have been a major socio-economic influence on the region. Mineral deposits have long been worked in the Pennine dales, and the rich coal resources of the Northumberland and Durham Coalfield underpinned the heavy industry of Tyneside,

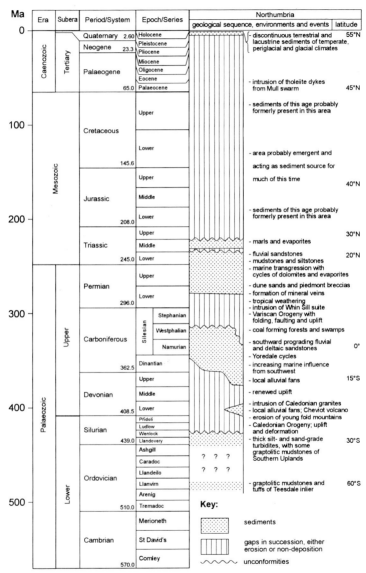

Figure 2 Geological column, and sequence of environments and events in Northumbria. Epochs/Series are shown as of equal length within Period/Systems for convenience only.

Wearside and Tees-side. The Permian has contributed also, with salt and **anhydrite** deposits formerly worked under Tees-side. The region is still in transition following the painful contraction of its powerful industrial base of the earlier 20th century.

The earliest geological events recorded in the rocks of the region are the final stages in the closure of an ancient seaway, the Iapetus Ocean, which separated the northern and southern halves of the British Isles in the Lower Palaeozoic (Fig. 3a). England, Wales and southeast Ireland were part of the microcontinent of Eastern Avalonia. This, together with Western Avalonia, moved northwards towards the equator from high southern latitudes, rapidly during the Ordovician and more slowly during the Silurian, as the ocean closed. Sediments deposited on the northern margin of the microcontinent, together with **subduction**-related volcanic rocks, are exposed in the Lake District and the west face of the Pennines, but only a very small **inlier** in Teesdale reveals a part of this sequence east of the Pennines in Northumbria. However, borehole evidence in central Durham proves rocks of this type at 860 m, thus showing they extend beneath the county at depth.

Scotland and northwest Ireland in the Lower Palaeozoic existed as parts of the margin of the Laurentian **plate**. During the later stages of closure and immediately afterwards, slices of the Laurentian plate margin were shuffled together along major **strike-slip faults**, producing the pattern of outcrops we see today. The Southern Uplands forms one of these slices, and along its southeastern margin Silurian rocks are exposed (Excursions 1, 2, 4, 10). These are thick **turbidites**, predominantly of sand-grade, with some shales, locally containing **graptolites**, sourced from rising land to the north and deposited in a narrow seaway, the remnant of the former ocean. Graptolites indicate a Llandovery age for outcrops on the coast between Siccar Point and St Abb's Head. Between Coldingham and Eyemouth, **acritarchs** suggest an early Wenlock age for some beds, but otherwise here and south to Burnmouth no diagnostic fossils have been found. Inland along the southeast margin of the Southern Uplands, scattered graptolite records indicate a Wenlock age. There are no records of younger Silurian sediments. Uplift, compression and deformation resulting from the collision of Eastern Avalonia and Laurentia affected the Southern Uplands area in late Silurian times and the Lake District-Teesdale area in the early Devonian. This **orogenic** episode concluded the long and complex **Caledonian Orogenic Cycle**, which resulted in a belt of fold mountains and uplands **striking** across the newly welded continental mass of Laurentia, Baltica and

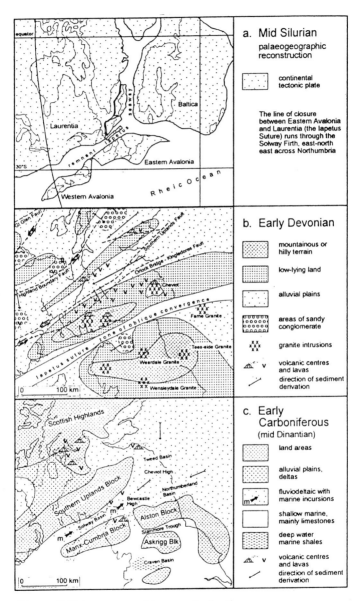

Figure 3 Palaeogeographic maps indicating:
(a) the distribution of continental plates in the mid Silurian (based on Scotese & McKerrow 1990 and other sources) and (b–f) the

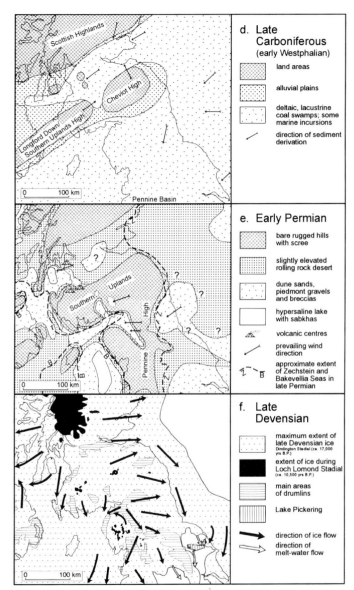

distribution of land and major sedimentary environments at various times in Northumbria and surrounding areas (based on Cope, *et al.* 1992 and other sources).

13

Avalonia, following the line of the former seaway. The area of the British Isles affected was from the Northern Highlands to North Wales.

As the Caledonian mountains rose, weathering under hot, arid conditions provided masses of debris which accumulated in alluvial fans in **intermontane basins**. These deposits constitute the Old Red Sandstone of Devonian age (Fig. 3b). In addition, the orogenic event caused melting within the crust which gave rise to early Devonian volcanic activity at the surface. The Cheviot area was one such volcanic centre, surrounded by thick sequences of **pyroclastic** rocks and lava flows, mainly of **andesitic** composition, and possibly exceeding 1000 m thick (Excursion 4). Erosion deep into the volcanic pile has revealed a slightly younger **granite** intrusion into the core of the complex which now crops out at its centre. Other late Caledonian granites were emplaced in the Lower Palaeozoic rocks of the Alston and Askrigg Blocks (now covered by a few hundred metres of Carboniferous sediments but detected geophysically and proved by boreholes), the Lake District, Southern Uplands, and under what is now the North Sea (Fig. 3b). North of Cheviot, early Old Red Sandstone **breccias, conglomerates**, red sandstones, **marls** and **calcretes** up to 600 m thick are associated with the volcanic rocks and rest with strong unconformity on folded Silurian sediments. West and north of Cheviot, these in turn are overlain by a second cycle of similar sediments, with common calcretes towards the top, unconformable on the Lower Old Red Sandstone, Cheviot volcanics and Silurian **greywackes** (Excursions 1, 2, 10). In places, this sequence contains evidence of a late Devonian age and is thus referred to the Upper Old Red Sandstone. Elsewhere it passes conformably upwards into early Carboniferous fluvial and **lacustrine** sediments. This second pulse of coarse debris reflects a phase of **tectonic** activity in the mid Devonian that rejuvenated the upland source areas.

By the early Carboniferous, relief on the Caledonian mountains had been somewhat reduced. A period of crustal extension followed the end of the orogenic cycle and broad, fault-bounded **half-graben** basins began to develop to the north and south of the Cheviot Block. Locally, conglomerates accumulated at the base of the Carboniferous sequence flanking the Cheviot (Excursion 9). The largest of these basins, the Northumberland Trough, developed along the line of the Iapetus **suture**, bounded to the northwest by the Southern Uplands and to the south by the Ninety Fathom-Stublick-Maryport Fault system, and the Alston and Manx-Cumbria Blocks. It was itself split into an easterly Northumberland Basin and a westerly Solway Basin by a basement ridge in the Bewcastle area (Fig. 3c). Extension appears to have been marked by the localized outpouring of **basaltic** lavas in the early Dinantian (Lower Carboniferous), cropping out along the northwestern margin of the Northumberland Trough (Excursion 10). Lower Carboniferous successions are much thicker in the more rapidly subsiding basins, and thinner and less complete on the intervening blocks.

The Tweed Basin, north of the Cheviot Block, with 1300 m of sediments, and the Northumberland Basin, with c.5000 m, have similar depositional histories. In the early Carboniferous, sediments derived from the north and east fed a broad coastal plain of channel sandstones and floodplain siltstones with frequent thin bands cemented by **dolomite** (**cementstones**) in the lower part of the sequence. Conditions remained arid and ephemeral lake and flood-plain deposits contain crystals of **gypsum**, anhydrite and **halite**, now as **pseudomorphs**. These form the Cementstone Group (Excursions 1, 2, 9), which in places in the Tweed Basin transitionally succeeds the Upper Old Red Sandstone. The climate became warmer and more humid during the Dinantian. Uplift of the source area in wetter conditions caused the **progradation** of a braided river system across the Northumberland Basin depositing the Fell Sandstone Group, a sequence dominated by planar and trough **cross-bedded** sandstones (Excursions 2, 9). These rocks now form significant high ground across mid Northumberland. Crossing into the Solway Basin, with about 7000 m of Carboniferous deposits, the Lower Border Group consists of interfingering sandstones, shales and thin limestones, the result of deltas prograding from the northeast and northwest into a shallow marine gulf (Excursion 5). Fossils in some of the limestones reflect close to normal marine conditions, but others contain **stromatolites** and mounds of vermiform 'gastropods' indicating fluctuating salinity. Thick sandstone bodies in the upper part of the Lower Border Group and the Middle Border Group result from westward progradation of the Fell Sandstone delta.

Later in the Dinantian, the marine influence from the southwest increased as the **clastic** supply from the north and east diminished. Repeated cycles of marine limestone, shale and sandstone in the Upper Border Group of the Solway Basin **transgressed** across the Northumberland Basin, where in addition, thick coals developed at the top of many cycles, and into the Tweed Basin, where proximity to the shore line is reflected in thinner limestones and more persistent coals. These sediments form the Scremerston Coal Group of the Northumberland and Tweed Basins (Excursions 3, 10), whose coals have been widely worked. In the succeeding Lower and Middle Limestone Groups (Excursions 3, 6, 7, 11), which are equivalent to the Liddesdale Group in the Solway Basin, the marine influence is further enhanced, with limestones thicker and coals thinner or absent. These are classic **Yoredale** cycles. By the late Dinantian, conditions had become increasingly uniform across Northumberland and the differentiation into basin and block less marked. At this time, the sea began to transgress across the Alston Block to the south and in the latest Dinantian, uniform Yoredale **facies** extended, from the still emergent but reduced land mass of the Southern Uplands, right across the whole of the Northumbrian area (Excursions 15–17). These changes mark the beginning of a gradual transition from extensional, fault-bounded basinal subsidence to a phase of much broader subsidence caused by cooling and contraction of lower crustal rocks which affected the whole of Northern England. However, despite uniformity of facies, thickness differences between block and basin areas persisted through much of the Namurian.

In Northumbria, the Yoredale cycles extend up into the Namurian as the Upper Limestone Group (Excursions 7, 11, 15–17). Although the thickest of all the Yoredale limestones, the Great, marks the base of the Namurian, upwards the limestones thin and the sandstones increase in thickness. Towards the top of the Namurian, marine influences and the limestones die out and the succession is dominated by cycles of erosive, coarse-grained, fluvial sandstones with interbedded fine sandstones, siltstones and mudstones. This is a thin northern equivalent of the Millstone Grit of the Central Pennines (Excursions 7, 15). There, the grit facies is developed throughout the Namurian and exceeds 2000 m in thickness. In Northumbria, the Namurian thins from just over 500 m in the subsurface near Newcastle to about 270 m on the Northumberland coast, of which only the top 50 m or so is of Millstone Grit facies.

By the beginning of the Westphalian, Northumbria was part of a broad Central Pennine Basin, in which maximum subsidence was in the Manchester area (Fig. 3d). There, the Coal Measures are over 3000 m thick, compared to some 875 m in the Northumberland and Durham Coalfield (Excursions 8, 15, 17). Cyclic sedimentation of shale/mudstone–sandstone–**seatearth**–coal, continued under the influence of deltaic processes, often as small fluvially dominated deltas prograding into fresh to brackish water flood plain lakes. Major distributaries are marked by ribbons of erosive, cross-bedded sandstones cutting down into the coal-bearing sequences. Marine bands are most common in the lower part of the succession, and where present can be correlated over large areas. There is a gradual shift to more fluvial dominated conditions higher in the Westphalian. The thickest and most productive coals occur in the lower half of the Middle Coal Measures. Coal mining in Northumbria was at its peak in the 19th and early 20th centuries. The last 30–40 years have seen a drastic reduction in underground working as first the inland mines became exhausted or uneconomic and most recently the larger coastal pits have been closed.

The volcanic and intrusive activity that had continued throughout much of the Carboniferous further south in England was absent in the north. Northumbria, however, was distinguished by a single, Permo-Carboniferous, intrusive event of considerable volume. This is the Whin **Sill** complex, a **tholeiitic dolerite** fed by **dykes** emplaced along approximately east–west extensional fractures formed at this time (Excursions 6, 10, 11, 16). The sill, in composite form, reaches 100 m thick and extends from Teesdale to the Scottish borders, abruptly changing its stratigraphical level via faults and **joints** from the mid Dinantian to the Lower Coal Measures. It is lowest in the sequence at its northern and southern extremities and highest around Alnwick (up to Namurian) and in the Midgeholme Coalfield (Fig. 1). The term 'sill' originated locally to describe any persistent hard bed (e.g. the Firestone Sill – a Namurian sandstone) and only subsequently took on its modern restricted meaning as an igneous rock.

Carboniferous, particularly Lower Carboniferous sediments of the Alston Block, also host the many **mineral veins** and **flats** of the North Pennine Orefield (Excursion 14). **Galena** was the main mineral, extracted for lead, but **sphalerite** was also common together with, in the central area, minor amounts of **pyrite, marcasite** and occasionally **chalcopyrite** and **pyrrhotite**. The **gangue** minerals are zoned, with **fluorite** predominating in the central part of the Alston Block, surrounded by **baryte, witherite** or **calcite**. The zoning was temperature related, with fluids reaching 220°C in the fluorite area, dropping to as low as 60°C on the margins of the orefield. Ore-bearing fluids are thought to have originated as brines forced out of the thick surrounding sedimentary basins, stripping out metals as they migrated through the Carboniferous, Lower Palaeozoic and granite rocks, and channelled towards the block along its bounding faults. High heatflow from the Weardale Granite, a Caledonian intrusion in the Lower Palaeozoic basement of the Alston Block, set up a convection cell with the hottest brines rising through the granite and the Dinantian sediments of the block at its centre. The main phase of mineralization was most likely Permian, although potentially mineralizing fluids are still circulating in the area. The deposits have been worked probably since Roman times and extraction peaked in the 19th century. Today the gangue minerals, fluorite and baryte, are the main resource; lead and zinc ores are produced as by-products.

Only part of the Upper Coal Measures and no Stephanian sediments are preserved in Northumbria. A period of uplift, tilting and folding, followed by deep weathering and erosion, occurred in late Carboniferous-early Permian times due to the compressional effects of the **Variscan Orogeny** to the south, and a major **eustatic** sea-level fall as water was locked up in the glaciation of the southern continent of Gondwana. A regional unconformity exists below the earliest Permian deposits, which overstep folded Coal Measures in the south of County Durham to rest on Namurian and locally Dinantian beds. Climatic conditions had changed from the tropical hot, wet regime of the Westphalian to a hot, arid regime in the early Permian as the British Isles drifted northwards from the equator. These conditions led to the formation of a zone of reddening 5–10 m, exceptionally 300 m, thick below the Permian unconformity. On this continental landscape, east of higher ground in the region of the Pennines, the surface had been reduced to a vast, rolling peneplain extending out into the area of the North Sea, on which the earliest sediments preserved are **lag** breccias and breccio-conglomerates (Fig. 3e). The succeeding Yellow Sands, now preserved as a series of east-northeast – west-southwest ridges up to 60 m thick in County Durham, are dune sands containing large-scale cross-bedded units indicating derivation from the east and northeast (Excursions 8, 13).

The beginning of the Upper Permian was marked by the rapid inundation of the low lying areas east and west of the Pennines (Fig. 3e). In the North Sea Basin, the Zechstein Sea reworked the upper part of the Yellow Sands. The deposits in the sea are strongly cyclic due to eustatic sea level rise and fall, resulting in the repeated expansion and contraction of the marine area under strongly evaporitic conditions. At the base of the first cycle is a very finely laminated deposit of alternating limestone or dolomite with organic rich layers, formed on the **euxinic** sea floor. This, the Marl Slate, is famous for the beautiful preservation of palaeoniscid fish, which swam in the oxygenated near surface waters, together with the remains of reptiles that fell or were transported into the sea. Euxinic conditions persisted throughout the first cycle in deeper parts of the basin but around the shallow oxygenated margins, **oolitic carbonates** developed, protected on their seaward side by a massive **bryozoan-algal** shelf edge reef, up to 100 m thick and more than 30 km long, that is well exposed in County Durham (Excursion 13). The cycle is completed by the basin-ward development of the Hartlepool Anhydrite, probably as a primary precipitate on the basin floor during a fall in sea-level. Four further cycles of carbonate and/or marl deposition, of decreasing thickness, with overlying and basin-ward **evaporites** are known. The carbonates are often oolitic and stromatolitic, with restricted faunas. Those of the second cycle pass into deeper water slope carbonates showing signs of slumping, and in which a wide range of **concretionary** structures are developed. At the top of the third cycle, the Billingham Anhydrite and overlying Boulby Halite have been extensively mined beneath Tees-side where they formed the basis for the local chemical industry. Further south in east Yorkshire, the halite gives way in its upper part to the Boulby Potash, which is mined at depth northwest of Whitby. Thus the third cycle represents the most complete development of an evaporitic mineral sequence in the region.

The cyclic deposits of the Upper Permian grade upwards into red marls with thin lenses of anhydrite and ultimately thick, dominantly fluvial sandstones of the Triassic Sherwood Sandstone Group in southeast Durham and Tees-side. These deposits are almost completely unfossiliferous and the Permo-Triassic boundary is placed as a matter of convenience at a distinctive level within the marls. The Sherwood Sandstone is succeeded, after a short break, by the Mercia Mudstone Group, a sequence of vari-coloured sandstones and red-brown and green marls, with beds of dolomite, anhydrite and evaporite residues in the lower part. These were the deposits of an extensive coastal plain, intermittently flooded by shallow saline waters from the southeast. Triassic rocks are now known almost exclusively from borehole evidence around Tees-side.

Younger deposits, excepting the widespread **glaciogenic** sediments of the recent past, are unknown in Northumbria, although evidence from outside the area suggests that the major marine transgressions of the Lower Jurassic and Upper Cretaceous may have covered the area. Any sediments deposited were subsequently removed, particularly during the Tertiary, when the northwestern parts of the British Isles underwent rapid uplift following the northward extension of Atlantic **seafloor spreading** between Greenland and Scandinavia. Associated igneous activity in centres in western Scotland extended its influence into Northumbria in the form of tholeiitic dykes, the best known being the Armathwaite-Cleveland Dyke in south Durham (Excursions 16, 17), and the Tynemouth and Acklington dykes in Northumberland. All have a similar late

Palaeocene age and appear to be far-flung representatives of the Mull dyke swarm.

A general trend in global cooling begun in the early Tertiary culminated in the sequence of cold and temperate climates which have affected the British Isles over the last 2.6 **Ma**. Several advances of ice probably covered Northumbria but almost all the deposits now preserved relate to the last extensive ice sheet glaciation in the late Devensian, around 17 000 yr **B.P.** (Fig. 3f; Excursion 12). In upland regions, most of the soils and unconsolidated deposits were stripped off and the hills and ridges moulded and streamlined. Ice, moving southwards from Scotland and the Cheviot, and extending into the westernmost part of the North Sea Basin, deflected to the southeast ice moving into the region from the Lake District and Galloway. Vast quantities of debris were deposited in the lowlands, as tills and water-laid deposits, smoothing out the pre-Quaternary relief of southeast Northumberland and eastern Durham. River valleys, some graded to cold stage sea levels down to −50 m O.D., were plugged by clays, sands and gravels. As the ice withdrew, most rivers re-established themselves close to their original courses. Ice melt resulted in the formation of widespread sheets of **glaciofluvial** sand and gravel, some now standing as terraces above the main rivers, and also areas of hummocky ice-contact deposits including **kames, kame terraces** and **eskers**, with many **kettle holes** and dead-ice hollows. The persistence of coastal and sea ice dammed the eastward drainage of meltwaters leading to the formation of lakes in low-lying areas. In these, laminated clays and silts were deposited with sand and gravel deltas and fans at the margins. In upland areas, fine series of **meltwater channels**, such as those around the Cheviots, were eroded mainly by water flowing beneath the ice during melting.

The main event of the present interglacial has been the rise in sea level to give the coastal morphology we see today. Evidence of the rise is found in submerged forests and peats, extending to at least −15 m O.D., present on the coasts of Northumberland and Durham. With a low tide, and not too much beach sand, these features can be readily seen in several places, such as Hartlepool, Seaburn, Blyth Beach, Cresswell, and Hauxley south of Amble. In the uplands, extensive peat deposits have formed in the higher, wetter areas.

1 · The geology of Siccar Point and Pease Bay

Brian Turner and **Colin Scrutton**
University of Durham

PURPOSE

This excursion will examine the spectacular and historically important 'Hutton's **Unconformity**', between Silurian **greywackes** and Old Red Sandstone at Siccar Point, and the stratigraphy and sedimentology of the fluvio-**lacustrine** Upper Devonian red beds and Lower Carboniferous Cementstone Group coastal alluvial plain sediments at Pease Bay.

LOGISTICS

The excursion, which is not recommended for large parties, can be completed in one short day. Private transport is essential. Siccar Point involves a steep descent, less daunting than it appears, down a 70 m high cliff. However, the unconformity can be seen clearly from the cliff top, from which there is an excellent view of the geology to the north. The Pease Bay section is tide-dependent and *should not be attempted during a rising tide*. It involves rough walking and scrambling, mostly over a boulder-strewn wave cut platform. The seaweed-covered rocks of the foreshore are slippery. The total distance covered is about 1 km and hard hats and waterproof footwear are strongly recommended.

Prior permission for access to Siccar Point should be sought from Robin Drysdale (Tel: 0136-83448), proprietor of the processing and packing plant for local swedes at Old Cambus Quarry. Note that the road into the quarry is used by heavy lorries.

Maps

O.S. 1:50 000 Sheet 67 Duns, Dunbar and Eyemouth; B.G.S. 1:50 000 Sheets 34 Eyemouth and 33E Dunbar.

GEOLOGICAL BACKGROUND

The area comprises **folded** and **faulted** Silurian greywackes of Llandovery age, unconformably overlain by Upper Old Red Sandstone which passes gradationally and conformably upwards into Lower Carboniferous Cementstones (Fig. 1.1). During Lower Palaeozoic times the area was located on the northwestern edge of the Iapetus Ocean. The ocean floor was being **subducted** beneath the Laurentian continental margin (Fig. 3a), with sediments of northerly derivation being deposited by **turbidity currents** in front of the subduction zone or alternatively in a **back-arc basin**. These Lower Palaeozoic greywackes contain **graptolites** and good examples of **Bouma sequences** indicative of a distal depositional setting. Whatever the origins of the sediments the ocean finally closed in late Silurian times resulting in the folding and faulting of the beds which

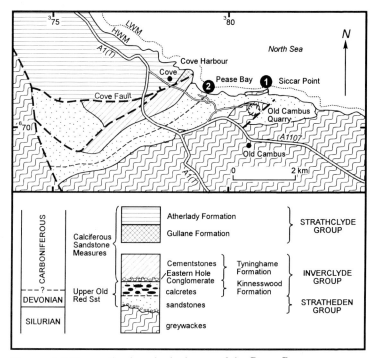

Figure 1.1 Generalized geological map of the Pease Bay–Siccar Point area.

show a steep northwesterly **dip**, becoming younger in that direction. However, the structure in this area is relatively simple and characterized by upright open folds with broad limbs and narrow hinge zones, and numerous high angle faults. When traced south towards Eyemouth the structure becomes more complex with shearing and fold axial thickening, amongst other complications. Ocean closure was also accompanied by volcanism, but evidence of this is not seen in this area.

This end Silurian **Caledonian Orogenic** event resulted in uplift and the establishment of continental conditions, followed by erosion, peneplanation and deposition of the fluviatile Upper Devonian red beds by ephemeral (flash-flood) braided streams, under semi-arid climatic conditions. By the beginning of the Lower Carboniferous the area was subjected to renewed **tectonism** and subsidence, with sediment derived from source areas to the north and east being deposited on a coastal alluvial plain. Climatic conditions remained unchanged from the Devonian to the early Carboniferous, as evidenced by the persistent presence of red beds in the Cementstones (see Excursion 2).

Stratigraphical interpretations vary, but the one adopted here is to place all the locally exposed Old Red Sandstone and Lower Carboniferous sediments in the Kinnesswood and part of the Tyninghame Formations of the Inverclyde Group, which range in age from late Devonian to early Carboniferous. The Kinnesswood Formation straddles the Devonian–Carboniferous boundary, with the top of the formation defined by a distinctive **calcrete** bed (Fig. 1.3A). In the past a thin **cementstone breccia** called the Eastern Hole **Conglomerate** has been taken as the **lithological** boundary between the Devonian and Carboniferous. This is now included in the Eastern Hole Beds of early Carboniferous age at the base of the Tyninghame Formation.

The area has a spectacular coastline characterized by steep rocky cliffs up to 70 m high, overlooking narrow rocky foreshores and occasional sandy beaches such as Pease Bay. Away from the coast the area has been terraced and extensively affected by glaciation, with most of the lower ground covered by **drift**. The higher ground behind has a typical rounded topography due to glacial erosion of the underlying solid bedrock, especially the Silurian greywackes. Mounds of coarse gravel, thought to be ice contact deposits (?**eskers**), stand up above the general level of the glacial terraces and at Pease Bay the glacial deposits are predominantly **till** overlying sands and gravel. Behind the sandy beach at Pease Bay is a shingle beach, now mostly grass-covered, which is one of the few examples of a raised post-glacial shoreline. Channels formed by glacial meltwater are common. Some are oriented perpendicular to the coastline and others, such as the one leading to Old Cambus Quarry, are oriented parallel to the coastline.

EXCURSION DETAILS

Locality 1, Siccar Point (NT 813710), **S.S.S.I.**, hammering prohibited. From the A1 just south of Cockburnspath take the A1107 towards Coldingham, turning onto the single track road to Pease Bay at NT 795702. Where the road turns sharp left downhill, continue straight on, along a single track road through an excellent example of a sub-glacial drainage channel into Old Cambus Quarry. The quarry and drainage channel are cut into a spur of Lower Silurian greywackes. Vehicles can be parked in the quarry by prior permission (see Logistics). Walk round the left-hand side of the buildings along the quarry wall, through the gate, and where the drainage channel broadens out, take the track slanting up the hill to the left and cross the fields to the cliff top at Siccar Point (the Scottish word *siccar* means safe).

Figure 1.2 Siccar Point: 'Hutton's Unconformity'. Near vertical Silurian greywackes unconformably overlain by gently dipping Upper Old Red Sandstone breccia and sandstone. *Photo:* C. T. Scrutton.

The view from the cliff top is spectacular, especially to the northwest where dark grey, folded and vertical Silurian greywackes can be seen, succeeded by brightly-coloured Old Red Sandstone sediments grading up into drab Lower Carboniferous Cementstones of the Pease Bay section. Further north beyond Pease Bay is Torness Power Station, one of the first nuclear power stations to be built in this country, the lighthouse at Barns Ness situated on Lower Carboniferous Limestone Group strata, and in the far distance the Bass Rock, a plug of **phonolitic trachyte** jutting sharply out of the sea.

The unconformity at Siccar Point (Fig. 1.2) was discovered by James Hutton (1726–1797), in the company of Sir James Hall and Professor John Playfair. Hutton, who farmed locally at Slighhouses for some 14 years, had long suspected the presence of an unconformity along this stretch of coast having already seen others at Arran in 1786 and Jedburg in 1787. In 1788 he and his companions sailed south from Dunglass, keeping close to the shore in order to examine the succession for signs of primary and secondary strata, and the contact between them. On landing at Siccar Point, they found near-vertical Silurian greywackes overlain by gently dipping Old Red Sandstone, the contact between them being marked by a distinct breccia. This locality enabled Hutton, one of the great pioneers of geological science, to develop his ideas on the cyclicity of major geological processes. Historically therefore, Siccar Point is a geological site of international importance, attracting geologists from all over the world.

A rough track leads down the cliff across the contours and the descent is easier than it appears at first sight from the cliff top, and well worth the effort. The exposures are on a seaward-dipping wave cut platform, where near-vertical Silurian greywacke sandstones, siltstones and shales, are unconformably overlain by a continental breccia and sandstone of Upper Old Red Sandstone age dipping gently seawards at about 15° (Fig. 1.2). The unconformity is estimated to represent a time gap of about 20 **Ma**. The Silurian rocks form laterally persistent beds of constant thickness, in which the sandstones form distinct ridges weathering out from the softer siltstones and shales. Lithological markers are lacking and correlation is difficult. The sandstones are predominantly medium to coarse-grained, normally graded, **quartz**-rich greywackes, containing a variety of sedimentary structures typical of turbidity current deposits, including horizontal laminations, ripple **cross-lamination, sole marks** such as **flutes** and grooves, and convolute lamination. Bedding surfaces are commonly covered with ripple marks which are straight, sinuous and

linguoid in plan. The succession consists of vertically stacked classic turbidite units in which the younging direction can be readily established. Graptolites, collected from the shales near Siccar Point and at the quarry, indicate an upper Llandovery age for the sediments.

The basal breccia, which commonly fills in local hollows and depressions on the original depositional surface, varies in thickness up to a maximum of about 6 m. It contains mainly angular, locally **imbricate** elongate **clasts**, deposited by currents flowing to the south and southeast. The clasts are predominantly of the underlying greywackes but with some **arkosic** sandstone, all set in a pink to red, coarse-grained **feldspathic** sandstone matrix. The overlying sandstone is a red, poorly sorted, feldspathic **arenite**, containing poorly defined laminations, small-scale cross-bedding and local **chert** lenses. The sandstone was deposited by braided, possibly ephemeral streams draining a semi-arid alluvial plain.

Return to the quarry, and at the end of the access road, turn right down hill to the Pease Bay caravan site.

Locality 2, Pease Bay (NT 795712). Parking for visitors is available at the caravan site free of charge. The Upper Old Red Sandstone and conformably overlying Lower Carboniferous Cementstones exposed in the cliffs and along the foreshore at the northern end of Pease Bay dip northwestwards at between 15–20° (Fig. 1.1). The sediments were deposited within the fault-bounded Oldhamstocks Basin on the northeast flank of the Southern Uplands. The age of the succession is poorly constrained and the Upper Old Red Sandstone here could be early Carboniferous in age.

The Old Red Sandstone consists of erosively based, multilateral and multistoried fining-upward sequences up to 4 m thick, composed of sandstone and siltstone. A **lag** of shale and siltstone **intraclasts**, with occasional small quartz pebbles and granules overlies the erosive base. Reworked calcrete nodules occur in channel lags higher in the succession. The sandstones above are predominantly pale red to maroon, locally mottled, fine to coarse-grained, immature and poorly sorted feldspathic arenites containing a patchy **dolomite** cement. Locally there is evidence of displacement along small faults and fractures. A small non-marine **bivalve** has been recovered from the sandstones at the northern end of Pease Bay. The sandstones contain mainly trough cross-bedding and show an overall fining-upward trend. Fine-grained, better sorted, friable white sands with well rounded grains are locally developed within the coarser-grained cross-bedded sands. These are interpreted as **deflation** deposits on the top of fluvial channel sand bars. The sandstones are sharply overlain by grey to purple overbank siltstones and silty mudstones showing red and green mottles and lenses, reflecting the oxidation state of the iron they contain. Some of the green mottles have carbonaceous plant material at their centres which gave rise to local reducing conditions within a predominantly oxidising environment. More extensive lenses probably owe their origin to shifts in position of the palaeo-watertable. The siltstones are mostly ripple cross-laminated, and increase in abundance towards the top of the Old Red Sandstone succession where the sandstones and siltstones become noticeably less red in colour. Here they are interbedded with hard, red to black calcrete which occurs in a number of forms according to its position in the succession.

Prominent calcretes first appear at the northern end of the small fault-controlled bay north of Pease Bay beach, as deep red to maroon and black nodules and thin nodular lenses, sometimes containing **pedogenic** tubules (rootlets). Higher up, the calcrete forms more continuous beds up to 1 m thick, the most mature containing irregular lenses of chert. They show a gradual increase in maturity towards the top of the succession (Fig. 1.3A), and even within individual calcretes there is often a vertical variation in the dominant form. Reworked calcretes are commonly concentrated on cross-bed foresets, at the base of sets and along the base of channel sands. In places long pedogenic tubules extend down through foresets for distances of more than 50 cm.

Because of their resistance to weathering the calcretes stand proud of the softer host rocks producing a typical knobbly surface texture, and unlike modern calcretes they have been dolomitized. The calcretes formed by leaching of **carbonate** from the upper part of the soil profile and its reprecipitation lower down. For extensive calcretes to develop extended periods of non-deposition are required, together with a warm, dry climate where the rainfall is not too seasonally peaked otherwise the carbonate may be leached from the soil profile. Geochemical analysis of selected calcretes and cementstones indicate that they formed from saline pore fluids (<100 ppm strontium).

Thin, laterally persistent cementstones also begin to make their appearance towards the top of the succession (Fig. 1.3A), which includes a well developed ripple cross-laminated, internally scoured lacustrine siltstone, located immediately below a thin, erosively-based cementstone breccia (Figs. 1.3B, 1.4). This breccia, c.20 cm thick, was formerly regarded as the lithological Devonian–Carboniferous

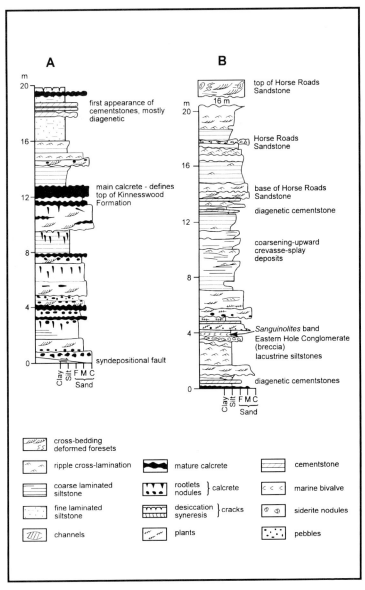

Figure 1.3 Measured sections of the (A) Upper Old Red Sandstone and (B) Lower Carboniferous Cementstones at the northern end of Pease Bay.

Figure 1.4 Rippled lacustrine siltstones overlain by cementstone breccia (Eastern Hole Conglomerate) within the Eastern Hole Beds at the base of the Tyninghame Formation, Pease Bay. *Photo:* B. R. Turner.

boundary. It contains flat, angular clasts of cementstone, laminated calcretized cementstone (?**algal**), pieces of carbonized wood and fish scales. The clasts are locally imbricate and cemented by ferroan dolomite giving the rock a distinctive yellowish-brown colour. The breccia now forms part of the Tyninghame Formation (Fig. 1.3B) and is thought to have been deposited on the dried-up bed of a lake, scoured by a major, but short-lived flood event that reworked and locally transported some of the dried-up lake bed material. Above the breccia is a thin, hard calcareous bed containing the bivalve *Sanguinolites*, recording the first fully marine conditions in the succession. Above, carbonaceous-rich, laminated siltstones and cementstones, some containing fish scales, fish spines and plant material, are composed of impure ferroan dolomite, pale grey in colour, and very hard and flinty. They consist of laminated cementstones of probable primary origin, and **concretionary** cementstones of early diagenetic origin. The latter type require pauses in sedimentation of hundreds of thousands of years for their formation, and unlike the cementstones 20 km to the south in the Tweed embayment, they are not associated with **evaporite** minerals.

At the northern end of the wave-cut platform, overlooking the entrance to Cove Harbour, a 47 m thick composite channel sandbody called the Horse Roads or Horse Road Sandstone cuts down into the underlying rippled siltstones (Fig. 1.3B). It is an **argillaceous**-rich, medium to coarse-grained sandstone with locally developed large brownish ironstone concretions which can be traced at intervals in the cliff face above the foreshore. Internally the sandstone is complex, containing trough cross-bedding, ripple cross-lamination, horizontal laminations, channelling and scouring, and locally deformed and overturned cross-bed **foresets**. Immediately north of the sandstone the Cove Fault **downthrows** strata some 900 m to the north, bringing in younger formations of the Strathclyde Group.

The Old Red Sandstone succession at Pease Bay was deposited by southwesterly flowing, distal sandy braided rivers, suggesting a source area, possibly including **granite**, somewhere in the present day North Sea. Deposition was interrupted periodically by contemporaneous tectonism diverting the river system to another part of the basin, thereby allowing time, and freedom from active sedimentation, for the formation of calcrete. Towards the top of the succession lakes were established on the braid-plain which received short-lived pulses of sediment during stream and sheet flood events. During drier periods the lake waters receded, resulting in increased salinities and the formation of cementstones. Fluvio-lacustrine conditions continued to dominate deposition in the Lower Carboniferous, with thin, overbank **crevasse-splay** sands and silts giving way towards the top of the succession to a thick deltaic or low sinuosity distributary channel sandbody deposited on the Lower Carboniferous coastal alluvial plain.

2 · The geology of Eyemouth and Burnmouth

Colin Scrutton and **Brian Turner**
University of Durham

PURPOSE

This excursion examines **folded** Silurian **greywackes** of the Hawick Group, early Devonian **autobrecciated** lavas **unconformably** succeeded by late Devonian (Old Red Sandstone) breccias, a transitional sequence across the Devonian–Carboniferous boundary, and an abandoned Pleistocene drainage channel.

LOGISTICS

Most are coastal outcrops and Locality 5 (Burnmouth Foreshore) requires low tide. Localities 1, 2 and 3 can be visited at half tide and Locality 4 is not tide-dependent. The itinerary described here should be adjusted to take account of tide times. Eyemouth has good parking with toilet and refreshment facilities. Parking at Burnmouth is possible along the side of the minor road. Parking at Burnmouth Harbour at the foot of the cliffs is limited.

The foreshore rocks may be slippery. Hard hats and wellingtons are essential. Localities 4 and 5 are not recommended for large parties.

Maps

O.S. 1:50 000 Sheet 67 Duns, Dunbar & Eyemouth; B.G.S. (Scotland) 1:50 000 Sheet 34 Eyemouth.

GEOLOGICAL BACKGROUND

By the early Silurian, the microcontinent of Eastern Avalonia, including the area of England, Wales and southeast Ireland, had moved northwards to lie in close proximity to the margin of Laurentia

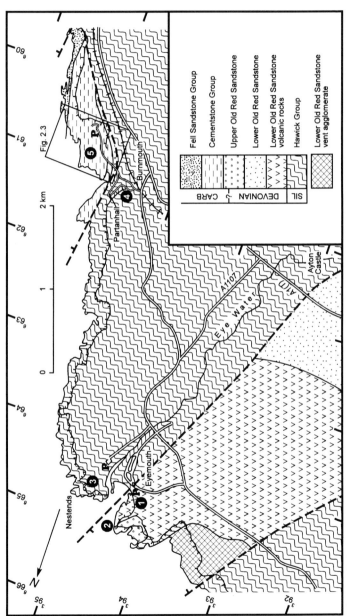

Figure 2.1 Geological map of the Eyemouth–Burnmouth area indicating the localities described.

(Fig. 3a). The intervening Iapetus Ocean had been reduced to the width of a narrow seaway. On the Laurentian side, thick deposits of poorly sorted sand grade sediments, derived from rising land to the north, began to cover the thin sequences of black, **graptolitic** shales that had accumulated on deep shelf and, in some places, oceanic crust. These coarser sediments were introduced by **turbidity flows**, each resulting in a few cms to 1 m+ thick greywacke, usually separated by thin bands of background mud-grade sediment, sometimes grapto-litic. In southern Scotland, these beds extend from the Llandovery up into the Wenlock when sedimentation ceased as the seaway narrowed, filled up and was eventually uplifted as a result of the final oblique compression between Avalonia, Baltica and Laurentia at the end of the **Caledonian Orogenic Cycle** (Fig. 3a). In the Southern Uplands, the Lower Palaeozoic rocks are arranged in a series of northeast–southwest trending **fault**-defined slices, variously interpreted as reflecting a syn-depositional **accretionary prism**, or the post-depositional **thrust** slicing of the thick sediment wedge on the Laurentian margin by the late Silurian compressional event. In the Eyemouth area, individual greywacke beds are seldom more than 0.5 m thick and are strongly folded; the sequence is unfossiliferous but is compared to the Hawick Group elsewhere and is thus most likely to be of Llandovery age.

Magmas generated at depth by the Caledonian continental col-lision resulted in extensive late Silurian/early Devonian intrusions and volcanic activity, represented by **dykes** and extensive lavas, **agglomerates** and **tuffs** in the Eyemouth area and, to the southwest, by the Cheviot Volcano (Excursion 4). Locally, contemporary sediments were largely derived from the newly formed volcanic centres. More earth movements in the mid Devonian produced gentle folds in the early Devonian rocks. In the late Devonian, this hilly landscape of Lower Palaeozoic greywackes and younger volcanic rocks was deeply weathered in a semi-arid climate and the debris stripped off by flash floods to form fans of breccias and channel sands on the lower ground. By the early Carboniferous, the relief was somewhat reduced and the Cementstone Group was deposited on a broad floodplain crossed by meandering to low sinuosity channels with the formation of early diagenetic **cementstones** during periods of non-deposition. Subsequently, rivers flowing from the east and northeast brought thick sequences of fluviodeltaic **cross-bedded** medium- to coarse-grained sandstones into the area, building out to the southwest. The Fell Sandstone Group succeeds the Cementstones on the coast south of Burnmouth.

A full Carboniferous sequence is developed further south in Northumberland. Locally, however, the next events of geological interest were the intrusion of late Carboniferous/?Permian basic dykes and the effects of the **Variscan Orogeny**. The latter resulted in local folding and faulting, but the most spectacular structure is the basement controlled, east **facing** Berwick **Monocline, striking** just west of north along the coast and responsible for the vertical Cementstone Group sequence at Burnmouth, where the steep limb is cut by a high-angle reverse fault.

Locally, the effects of the Pleistocene glaciation include a variable covering of **till**, thick in the valleys but thin and patchy on the high ground extending to the coast at Burnmouth. An infilled pre-Devensian river valley occurs in Eyemouth bay. The present form of Burnmouth Glen and the Eye Water gorge below Ayton are the result of post-glacial deepening of older valleys.

Further details will be found in Greig (1988; in McAdam *et al.* 1992).

EXCURSION DETAILS

From the A1 about 11 km north of Berwick, take the A1107 to Eyemouth. Cross the Eye Water and turn right. At the church keep straight on to the northern end of the town, then turn sharply back to the right to the car park with toilets and cafe on the esplanade (NT 944645).

Locality 1, Eyemouth Beach (NT 944646). From the car park, turn left and walk to a point where access to a corner of the beach can be obtained via a ramp (Fig. 2.1). On the lower foreshore and in the cliffs where they rise towards the north are extensive exposures of rocks of agglomeratic texture which have been interpreted by Greig (1988) as autobrecciated lavas of early Devonian age. Around mid-low tide level, exposures are heavily coated with seaweed, but at the edge of the beach are a number of good, sand polished surfaces in which the fragments are relatively small, angular to rounded and variable in shape, set in an **igneous** matrix. These dark coloured, reddish weathering rocks with scattered green reduction spots are **pyroxene andesites**, with well formed **phenocrysts** of plagioclase **feldspar**. Some outcrops have the appearance of debris flows of **volcaniclastic** material. Further north round the bay and in the cliffs, however, the rocks are paler, purplish grey **dacites**, more acid in composition. **Clast** size increases, some in excess of 1 m across, and most are tabular with little intervening matrix. They show good flow-banding, with aligned feldspar, **hornblende** and **biotite** phenocrysts.

In the back of the bay, the volcanic rocks in the cliff are cut by a channel reaching to beach level. The softer fill, of strikingly reddened layers of unconsolidated breccio-**conglomerates** and sands capped by several metres of **till**, is weathered back to form a gully. The mixture of angular and rounded clasts in the coarse unit accessible at beach level is dominated by fragments, <30 cm, of Silurian grey-wackes, fine–medium grained red sandstones and volcanic rocks, with a vague **imbrication** indicating water flow towards the sea. The channel is interpreted as that of a pre-Devensian stream.

Locality 2, Eyemouth Fort (NT 944649). Proceed with care across the foreshore to a small bay on the point beneath the fort, where the unconformity between the autobrecciated volcanic rocks, here with individual blocks several metres in length, and the overlying red breccias and sandstones of the Upper Old Red Sandstone can be seen. The deposits represent alluvial fans of a semi-arid environment, fed by flash floods stripping material from the surrounding hills. The texture of the Devonian rocks can be studied in the many fallen blocks. Towards the far end of the small bay, a large **joint** face shows excellent imbrication in the breccias indicating flow from the east. The clasts are similar to those in the Pleistocene channel but more dominantly greywackes, with red sandstones and volcanic rocks. At some levels, where the fines have been washed out of the deposit, they are cemented by **calcite**.

The small offshore islands are of Silurian greywackes just on the east side of the westerly downthrowing, north-northeast trending Eyemouth Fault which is responsible for juxtaposing the Devonian rocks against the Silurian greywackes seen on the east side of Eyemouth harbour.

Return to the car park in Eyemouth and drive out of the village to the A1107. Turn left, cross the Eye Water and then immediately left again down The Avenue. Follow the road to a parking point (NT 947643) on the east bank of Eyemouth harbour just before the old Customs House.

Locality 3, Nestends (NT 950647). Walk in front of the Customs House straight ahead to Nestends, then follow the cliff-edge path southeast round the golf course. Superb exposures of folded and faulted Silurian greywackes of the Hawick Group can be seen from the cliff top and along the promontories, with access to foreshore level possible in several bays. The rocks are fine sand-grade **turbidites** of varying thickness with reddish mudstone interbeds; no diagnostic fossils have been found. Graded bedding is apparent in places and some units have poorly developed **sole structures** at the base and small scale ripples and channels towards the top, all indicating way up. The folds **strike** east-northeast–west-southwest and have a complex form, due to a significant sinistral shear element during compression. They are tight, almost **isoclinal** in places, with highly variable 1–15 m wavelengths as folds develop or die out along strike. Fold axes vary considerably in their **plunge** and in some cases, the **cleavage**, which is well developed in the mud grade beds, is folded. Just beyond the end of the golf course, in a north–south zone about 150 m wide west from Agate Point (NT 955642), the shearing associated with the compressional event has resulted in the juxtaposition along strike of southwest plunging folds which are upward-facing with downward-facing folds plunging to the northeast (Fig. 2.2). These are probably **sheath folds** and all these features are the result of a single phase of deformation.

From Agate Point, follow the wall along the southern edge of the golf course into the housing estate, then turn right to reach the car park. Return to the A1107, turn left and after 1 km turn left again onto the Burnmouth road. Park on the roadside where the houses of Burnmouth start on the left (NT 953612).

Figure 2.2 Downward facing Silurian greywackes of the Hawick Group at Agate Point, Eyemouth (Locality 3). *Photo:* C. T. Scrutton.

Locality 4, road cutting below Burnmouth Hill (NT 957611). Immediately north of the railway bridge, take the road to the east that descends steeply to the shore (Fig. 2.1). At the top of the hill, fork left and follow the narrow road downhill with outcrops of Silurian Hawick Group greywackes **dipping** predominantly about 65° northwest on the left. After some 180 m, approach a roadside outcrop on a left-hand bend, where the first beds are near vertical and younging towards the sea. A 0.7 m greywacke sandstone bed has excellent **flute marks**, suggesting turbidity flow from the northeast; these sole structures can be traced around the folds here and are well seen just off the road lower down the hill. Viewed along strike, the cleavage in the soft, shaly interbeds can be seen refracting and dying out in the more competent greywacke sandstones. Immediately downhill is a synclinal axis, cut on its seaward side by a 4.25 m wide Siluro-Devonian **porphyrite** dyke, in which the chilled margin and the coarser centre with plagioclase feldspar phenocrysts can be compared. Beyond the dyke is the nose of a small **anticline** followed immediately by a sharp syncline with a faulted axis. It is in the seaward limb of this **syncline** that the sole structures can be well seen.

If time and tide allow, descend the hill to where similar rocks can be studied on the foreshore north of Partanhall (NT 958612). Here the cross-cutting relationships of the porphyrite intrusions, roughly parallel to the north–south strike of the Silurian greywackes, can be seen, together with a later generation (late Carboniferous-?Permian) of east–west **quartz dolerite** dykes. On the foreshore at low tide, the northward extension of the faulted Berwick Monocline can be seen with the Carboniferous Cementstone Group on the seaward side.

From the foot of the hill at Partanhall, cross to Burnmouth Harbour (NT 959609). Alternatively, return to the vehicle and take the road down to Burnmouth Harbour, or to Cowdrait at the end of the narrow tarred road along the seafront, where there is limited parking for one or two cars or a minibus.

Locality 5, Burnmouth Foreshore (NT 958611). At low tide the foreshore section provides continuous exposure over a distance of some 2 km, and involves rough walking and scrambling over vertically dipping and differentially eroded, wet, slippery rocks.

The sediments exposed include the Upper Old Red Sandstone and Lower Carboniferous Cementstone Group, overlain by the Fell Sandstone Group (Fig. 2.3). The sediments young seawards on the steep northerly limb of the east-facing Berwick Monocline, with the beds vertical to slightly overturned and dipping between 55° and 80°

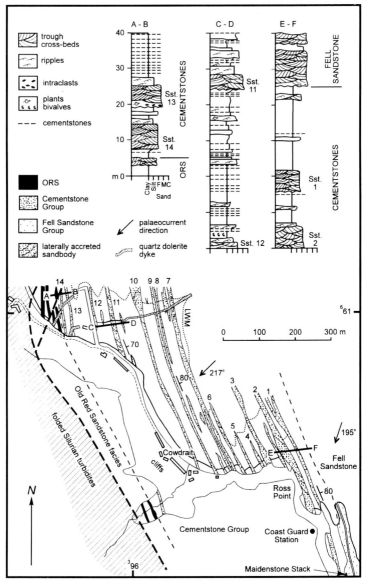

Figure 2.3 Generalized geological map and sections of the foreshore exposures of the Cementstone and Fell Sandstone Groups at Burnmouth.

to the west-northwest and west-southwest. The structure is most tightly compressed in the north where it is also more extensively faulted.

The upper 50 m of Old Red Sandstone, exposed on the foreshore west of Burnmouth Harbour (Fig. 2.3), contains up to five relatively poorly exposed fining-upward sequences, each comprising an erosively based, coarse-grained, trough cross-bedded fluvial channel sandstone overlain by fine-grained fluvio-**lacustrine** sandstones, siltstones and silty mudstones containing **calcretes** similar to those at Pease Bay (Excursion 1). The Old Red Sandstone on the foreshore is faulted and intruded by a northeast–southwest trending quartz dolerite dyke. Further west in the hillside above the harbour Old Red Sandstone is faulted against the Silurian greywackes.

The Old Red Sandstone is conformably overlain by the Lower Carboniferous Cementstone Group which is completely exposed on the foreshore to a total thickness of 450 m. The best exposures, to the east and south of the harbour, consist of **micaceous**, fluvial channel sandstones regularly interbedded with fluvio-lacustrine overbank siltstones, mudstones, sandstones and subordinate cementstones composed of ferroan **dolomite**. The succession is characterized by a crudely cyclic pattern of deposition of the type cementstone-mudstone-sandstone-mudstone-cementstone. The cementstones are extremely hard and splinter when hit. They consist of a number of different but gradational types, including sandy and banded cementstones, which contain a variety of sedimentary structures. A typical sequence comprises massive structureless cementstone at the base, overlain by flat laminations and convolute laminations at the top. Cementstone beds are <45 cm thick and in parts of the succession they have a nodular appearance, and locally contain vugs lined with calcite **pseudomorphs** of original **evaporite** minerals such as **gypsum**. Lateral accretion surfaces, indicative of point bar deposition and meandering river channels, have been identified in some sandbodies seen on aerial photographs but they are extremely difficult to recognize in the field because of the steep dip of the beds. Burrows, rootlets, **bivalves**, fish fragments and mudcracks have been found in the overbank fines, but vary in abundance through the succession. The lower part is predominantly **argillaceous** and red to purple in colour. It contains thin (<30 cm) cementstones yielding rare fish fragments and bivalves. Joints in one cementstone bed near the east wall of the harbour are coated with **galena**. Plants are common throughout this part of the succession which contains three major sandbodies up to 7.7 m thick. Two of them are relatively simple, single storey, fining-upward sandbodies containing trough cross-bedding overlain by ripple cross-lamination. Channel sandstone 11 (Fig. 2.3) contains a well developed local lenticular basal channel **lag** conglomerate whilst the other one, next to the east wall of the harbour, is more complex in its internal organisation (Fig. 2.3, sandstone 12).

In the middle part of the succession the mudrocks are mostly grey and sandy, and the associated cementstones thicker and more abundant. Cementstones reach a maximum stage of development here and beds containing bivalves and **serpulids** become more common. Only two major fining-upward channel sandstones occur in that part of the succession, both cross-bedded in the lower part and ripple cross-laminated in the upper part, with local hard calcareous lenses. Towards the top of the succession the beds are typically calcareous. They contain a greater abundance of rootlets but bivalves and fish fragments are rare. The finer grained beds are generally red, purple and green, often variegated and mottled, but the associated cementstones are much less common and thinner. Major channel sandstones increase in abundance and thickness up-section. They differ from those in the lower part in the following ways: they have a well developed sheet-like geometry with scoured bases locally overlain by **intraclast** conglomerates; they commonly have a more complex, internally scoured, multistoried form with less evidence of lateral accretion surfaces; and they show little sequential ordering of stratification types which are dominated by low angle trough cross-bedding and ripple cross-lamination. The change in character of the sandbodies through the succession suggests that they were deposited by channels of variable sinuosity and size, but with a general trend towards larger, less sinuous channels towards the top of the succession. These changes relate to base level changes in response to **tectonic** and/or climatic factors heralding deposition of the Fell Sandstone Group. The presence of cementstone intraclasts in channel sands, and the inverse relationship between the abundance of sandstones and cementstones, indicates an early **diagenetic** origin for the cementstones during significant periods of non-deposition. They were precipitated below the sediment-water interface in interdistributary lakes and lagoons on a low relief, semi-arid coastal alluvial plain.

The Fell Sandstone Group **conformably** overlies the Cement-stones, with a sharp but locally erosive contact. Some of the best exposures occur on the foreshore by Maidenstone Stack (Fig. 2.4), where the base of the Fell Sandstone cuts down 2–3 m into the underlying Cementstones. This is the most northerly exposure of Fell Sandstone in the Tweed Basin and one of the few localities where the contact between the Fell Sandstone and the Cementstones can be

Figure 2.4 View north of Maidenstone Stack, c.15 m high, composed of near vertical Fell Sandstone. The erosive contact with the underlying Cementstone Group is at the stack foot on the left. *Photo:* B. R. Turner.

clearly seen. The Fell Sandstone here comprises two, erosively based fining-upward sequences, but only the lower sequence and the base of the overlying one is completely exposed at low tide. The lower sequence, about 10 m thick, consists of planar and trough cross-bedded, medium to locally coarse-grained pebbly sandstone containing intraclasts of cementstone. The grain size and scale of the cross-beds decreases towards the top of the sandbody which is overlain by up to 50 cm of rippled and horizontally laminated fine sandstone, siltstone and silty shale, with reddish mottling at the top. Above is the erosive, intraclast-strewn base of the cross-bedded sandstone at the bottom of the overlying sequence. Some cross-beds show evidence of liquefaction and deformation, contemporaneous with deposition. The Fell Sandstone was deposited within a tectonically active environment by perennial braided streams flowing to the southwest, in a similar direction to the Cementstone channels (Fig. 2.3). The sandstones, less micaceous and more feldspathic than those in the Cementstone Group, sparkle due to the reflection of light from secondary crystal faces deposited in optical continuity on detrital quartz grains.

When returning to the cliff top, note that the road joins the A1 at the Flemington Inn 300 m to the south.

3 · The Carboniferous rocks around Berwick-upon-Tweed

Brian Turner and **Colin Scrutton**
University of Durham

PURPOSE

This excursion examines the sedimentology, palaeontology and structure of the Lower Carboniferous succession in the Tweed Basin.

LOGISTICS

Localities 1–5 represent a good half-day and Localities 6–7 a full-day excursion. Berwick on the north side of the River Tweed estuary and Tweedmouth–Spittal on the south both have easy parking, and full facilities are available at all but Cocklawburn Beach (Locality 7). All the localities are on the coast and require low to mid tide. The rocky foreshore can be slippery; wellingtons and hard hats are recommended.

Maps

O.S. 1:50 000 Sheet 75 Berwick-upon-Tweed; B.G.S. 1:50 000 Sheet 1/2 Berwick-upon-Tweed and Norham (Solid and Drift).

GEOLOGICAL BACKGROUND

In late Devonian and early Carboniferous times the structure of northern England consisted of a number of basins and blocks. The largest of these basins, the Northumberland Basin, was separated from the smaller Tweed Basin to the north by the Cheviot axis. This remained a positive area until late Asbian times, when regional subsidence occurred and the two basins merged into one. The Northumberland Basin owed its origin to Carboniferous extensional re-activation of a northerly dipping crustal scale shear zone. A similar

42

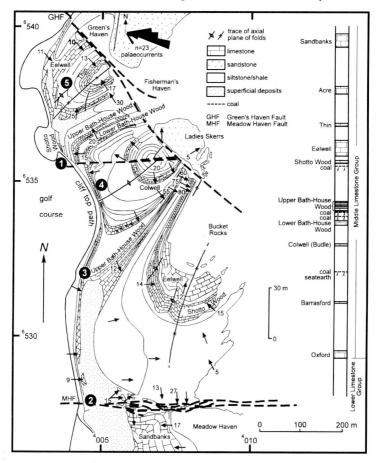

Figure 3.1 Geological map and section of the Meadow Haven–Green's Haven area, Berwick-upon-Tweed.

origin is favoured for the Tweed Basin, which is interpreted to have formed in response to reactivation of a thrust slice in the Southern Uplands.

Up to 2200 m of Lower Carboniferous sediments were deposited in the Northumberland Basin and 1300 m in the Tweed Basin. Lower Carboniferous Dinantian stratigraphy in both basins is the same and consists of the Cementstone Group, the Fell Sandstone Group, the

Scremerston Coal Group and the Lower and Middle Limestone Groups. The sequence seen on this excursion, from the top of the Scremerston Coal Group to the base of the Namurian Upper Limestone Group, records a series of marine **transgressions** and **regressions** across a lower delta plain environment, resulting in vertically stacked **Yoredale cyclothems** comprising a shallow marine **bioclastic** limestone, overlain by mudstone, siltstone and sandstone capped by a **seatearth** and coal. The marine influence progressively increases up-section.

Berwick-upon-Tweed lies on the north bank of the River Tweed and is one of Britain's most historic towns. It was constantly fought over during the Anglo-Scottish wars of the Middle Ages, changing hands some 13 times until 1482 when it was taken by the English; since then it has remained part of England. One of the most impressive features of the town is the Elizabethan walls, built 1558–1570; other features of interest include the Georgian Town Hall, the Barracks (the first to be purpose-built in Britain), the Royal Border viaduct railway bridge built by Robert Stephenson and the 300-year-old low-level stone bridge across the Tweed built of Old Red Sandstone.

EXCURSION DETAILS

Locality 1, Berwick cliff top, overlooking Green's Haven (NU 004537) and Fisherman's Haven (NU 004536). From the A1, turn off to Berwick on the A6105 (Fig. 3.3). Immediately after crossing over the railway bridge turn left towards Berwick Holiday Centre. Turn right past the centre across the municipal golf course to the cliff top where limited parking is available. Alternative parking is available in The Parade between the Barracks and Holy Trinity Church: access to the cliff top is through Walkergate and across the golf course.

The Lower Carboniferous Middle Limestone Group succession exposed on the foreshore at Berwick ranges from the sandstone below the Oxford Limestone to the Acre Limestone (Fig. 3.1). From the cliff top at low tide, the spectacularly **folded** and **faulted** upper Middle Limestone Group strata can be seen on the foreshore at Green's Haven. A series of domes and basins is defined by the outcrop pattern of the more resistant limestone beds (Fig. 3.2). The most prominent of these is the Eelwell Limestone which is exposed at intervals along the coast south of the Tweed (for example Locality 7), and further south at Beadnell Bay.

Figure 3.2 Ladies Skerrs dome (Locality 4) from the clifftop at
Berwick (Locality 1). *Photo:* C. T. Scrutton.

Locality 2, Meadow Haven Bay (NU 007527). Walk south along the
cliff top path from Locality 1 to the Meadow Haven fault zone (Fig.
3.1) where the steep cliffs change to slope features, and a footpath
allows easy access to the beach. Beware of golfers and golf balls when
walking along the cliff top path! The first outcrops associated with the
Meadow Haven Fault zone occur at the base of the cliff and consist of
reddish and white, rippled and **cross-bedded** sandstones and
siltstones containing locally developed, deep-red iron oxide **concretions** and burrow structures, which become particularly common
in the upper part. **Ganister** can be seen adjacent to part of the
Meadow Haven fault zone which comprises sheared and faulted
blocks showing both oblique slip and dextral movement. On the north
side the beds **dip** into the fault plane, cut by a number of small tension
faults. Shales, containing thin rippled silty and sandy interbeds and
lenses, and a few brown ironstone nodules and lenses, are exposed in
the unstable cliff face. These are underlain by the Upper Bath-House
Wood Limestone which rises in the cliff c.30–40 m to the north. It is a
hard, **argillaceous biomicrite** with a soft shaley top containing
crinoid ossicles, **brachiopods**, **gastropods**, **corals** and **bivalves**.
Bedding surfaces are covered with the swirling traces of *Zoophycos*

caudagalli (locally called cock's tails), ubiquitous to all the limestones in the succession. They are the feeding burrow systems of an unknown worm-like organism.

Locality 3, Bucket Rocks syncline (NU 008532). At this locality the lower leaf of the Upper Bath-House Wood Limestone thins and passes into calcareous shale. A 21 cm thick coal seam and root-penetrated **fireclay** or seatearth, stained yellow by **jarosite**, occurs beneath the calcareous shale. The fireclay passes down into a cross-bedded and ripple cross-laminated sandstone spotted with reddish iron oxide burrow infills. The sandstone, which was deposited by palaeocurrents flowing to the southeast, is underlain by a calcareous sandstone with ripples in the coarser, more sandy parts. Two small faults, **downthrowing** to the north, drop the Upper Bath-House Wood Limestone to the base of the cliff on the north side of the point below the coastguard lookout. Here, it is a rubbly-looking fossiliferous limestone, the upper part of which has been selectively **dolomitized**; the presence of cavities suggest local de-dolomitization. Fossils occur scattered throughout the limestone or concentrated into distinct bands, whilst bedding surfaces are covered with superb *Zoophycos* feeding traces. Another feature of the limestone is the presence of numerous **stylolite** seams.

Locality 4, Ladies Skerrs dome (NU 008536). South of the southerly-downthrowing normal fault, the following sequence can be seen in the cliff; burrowed shales, the Lower Bath-House Wood Limestone, c.6 m fossiliferous shales, then the Upper Bath-House Wood Limestone. The latter consists of two limestone units. A 1 m lower leaf is underlain by a 1–3 cm coal. It is separated by 1.5 m of shales from the upper leaf which consists of three beds separated by shaley partings. Bedding surfaces show abundant horizontal burrow traces.

Locality 5, Green's Haven Bay (NU 004538). North of the fault, the Upper Bath-House Wood Limestone forms the prominent, well **jointed** bedding plane surface, dipping 21° northwest. The overlying shales are marine with rare brachiopods at the base, but thin ironstone bands a little higher up suggest a decreasing marine influence. Further north, tiny rippled silty lenses (starved ripples) occur in the thick shales and thicker siltstone, and fine sandstone interbeds with plane laminations, ripples and convolute laminations appear; some of the thicker interbeds have burrowed and **bioturbated** tops. Towards the top of this sequence, where the shales become more sandy, a thick unit, containing bulbous **concretions**, is extensively burrowed and bioturbated obliterating most of the primary sedimentary structures. This is overlain by a thick, 2 m seatearth with black rootlet traces, and a thin 2–20 cm coal. Black, locally burrowed shales beneath the Shotto Wood Limestone succeeded by more shale are exposed approaching the steps (Fig. 3.1). The Eelwell Limestone is brown, vuggy and dolomitized in much of its outcrop, but on the northwest side of the paddling pool, it is un-dolomitized and contains abundant *Gigantopro-ductus* brachiopods, together with scattered corals including *Siphono-dendron junceum* (a distinctive branching coral with close-spaced corallites about 3 mm in diameter). At the northern end of Green's Haven Bay shales occur adjacent to the southwest side of the northwest–southeast trending Green's Haven Fault; on the northeast side is a softish, **feldspathic**, medium to coarse and locally pebbly, trough and rarely, planar cross-bedded sandstone deposited by currents flowing from the west-northwest (Fig. 3.1). The fault plane dips 65° southwest, and shows a dominant oblique slip movement with some dextral translation. The fault can be traced southeast via small reefs of rock into the dome at Ladies Skerrs.

From the parking area return to the A1167 (old A1) through Berwick, cross the Tweed Bridge and continue south (Fig. 3.3). At the roundabout (NT 996516) turn left for Spittal and continue to the end of Main Street where there is parking (NU 009510).

Locality 6, Spittal. South from here for 4 km, there is almost complete foreshore exposure from the top of the Scremerston Coal Group, through the Lower and Middle Limestone Groups, and into the basal Upper Limestone Group. If possible, a second vehicle parked at Cocklawburn Beach (Locality 7) will enable a single continuous traverse to be made.

Some 30 m of shales, sandstones, seatearths and thin coals of the Scremerston Coal Group are exposed on the foreshore north of Huds Head. The first limestone, the 1.5 m, crinoidal, Dun Limestone, marks the base of the Lower Limestone Group (Fig. 3.3). It forms a foreshore feature dipping 30° offshore, but is best seen where it rises in the cliff on the north side of Huds Head, where a seatearth and 36 cm coal is visible immediately beneath it. A band rich in the coral *Siphonodendron junceum* occurs near the base, together with large productid brachio-pods and scattered other fossils. Brachiopods also occur in the shales above. The Dun Limestone cycle is the first of a series of coarsening-upward cycles consisting of marine limestone, shales, usually with ironstone bands and nodules, silts, sands, often first as starved ripples,

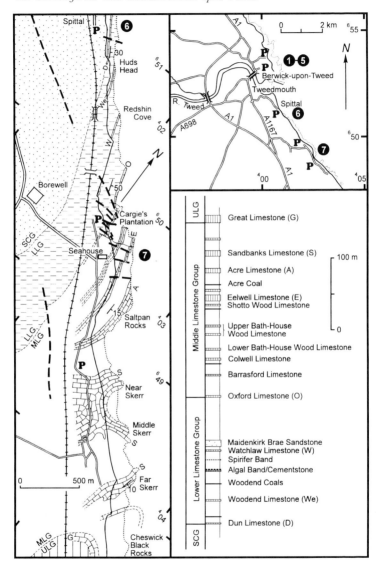

Figure 3.3 Geological map and section of the Spittal–Cocklawburn Beach coastal section. S.C.G. = Scremerston Coal Group; L.L.G, M.L.G., U.L.G. = Lower, Middle and Upper Limestone groups respectively. Inset map of the Berwick-upon-Tweed area.

lenticular and/or tabular units of cross-bedded sandstone, then usually a seatearth and coal. The environmental change at the base of the Limestone Groups is a subtle increase in marine influence and decrease in periods of emergence. Scattered thin coals occur throughout the succession and the limestones, at least below the level of the Oxford Limestone, are relatively thin and well spaced with thick intervening shales and sandstones, some showing strong channel form.

This lower part of the sequence can be traced in relatively undisturbed north-northwest **striking** beds across the foreshore south to the far side of Redshin Cove. The thick sandstones above the Dun Limestone forming Huds Head contain intersecting lenticular fine-grained cross-stratified units near the base and medium to coarse grained, multistoried, mainly planar cross-bedded sets deposited by migrating channel bars towards the top. In the cliff above, a major distributory channel filled with small-medium scale, mainly trough cross-bedded sandstones cuts down to the south through the shales overlying the prograding deltaic sequence. Opposite a prominent embayment where the cliff is replaced by a grassy slope, a prominent calcrete is overlain by the Woodend Limestone, which forms a feature on the foreshore, striking into the cliff to the south. This limestone is notable for its excellent fauna of fasciculate corals, mainly *Siphonodendron junceum* but also *S. martini* (with corallite diameters 7–8 mm). Many of the *S. junceum* colonies are virtually uncrushed and in position of growth. Towards the top of the limestone, and particularly on the top bedding surface, scattered colonies of *Lithostrotion maccoyanum* (massive with polygonal corallites 3–4 mm diameter) occur. The solitary corals *Dibunophyllum* (with a spider's web axial structure) and *Caninia* (no axial structure) are present together with the calcareous **sponge** *Chaetetes septosus*.

The Woodend Limestone is overlain by another classic coarsening-upward sequence ending with the Woodend Coals, associated with slumping in the grassy and degraded cliff and thus poorly exposed. About 15 m higher in the succession is a 1.2 m **cementstone** band and some 2 m higher a very distinctive 50 cm Algal Band, consisting of subspherical **algal oncolites**, up to 9 cm diameter, which become more densely packed towards the top of the bed. A 4.5 m black oil shale, forming a broad slack on the foreshore, succeeds the Algal Band. In the sequence above, the Watchlaw Limestone can be identified just before a prominent step on the foreshore onto the thick sequence of cross-bedded sandstones of the Maidenkirk Brae Sandstone. Further progress south is difficult and only possible at low tide.

In the corner of the cove just beyond the step, climb a grassy dip slope to the cliff top path. From here, the lenticular nature of beds below the Watchlaw Limestone can be clearly seen on the foreshore to the north.

For those with a single vehicle, return to it and rejoin the A1167 at the roundabout and turn south for Scremerston. After 2 km turn left at a signpost for Cocklawburn Beach and rejoin the coast at Seahouse. Turn left, cross a cattle grid and proceed c.150 m into a field from where there is a cliff path down to Cargie's Kiln, or right to where vehicles can be parked at various points on the roadside opposite Saltpan Rocks and the Skerrs.

Locality 7, Cargie's Plantation (NU 019498) to Cocklawburn Beach (NU 036478). Descend to the foreshore at Cargie's Plantation to continue the section southwards (Fig. 3.3). The sequence here beneath the Oxford Limestone is confused by a series of small east–west to northwest–southeast faults. At Cargie's Kiln, the 5 m thick, poorly fossiliferous but crinoidal Oxford Limestone marks the base of the late Dinantian Middle Limestone Group. The limestone is split into **posts** by shaley partings, one of which near the base of the limestone contains particularly prominent rolled algal nodules. In the limestone, red algal haloes around bioclasts stand out on wave polished surfaces. The Middle Limestone Group consists of cycles in which the limestones are thicker and more laterally persistent on a county-wide scale than in the Lower Limestone Group and the sandstones thinner, although thin coals are still developed at the tops of some cycles.

Several thin limestones dipping between 30–60° east-northeast intervene between the Oxford and the next thick limestone, the Eelwell. Each forms the base for a coarsening-upward cycle, often with well developed ripples, small-scale lenticular cross-bedded sets and **hummocky cross-stratification** (Reynolds 1992) developed in the sandstones, a seatearth and sometimes a thin coal. Following each transgression, the fluvio-deltaic processes carrying progressively coarser clastic material into the basin now show more evidence of shoreline, particularly storm dominated reworking, and less evidence of distributary channel, interdistributary bay and floodplain sediments than in lower parts of the succession (Reynolds 1992).

The Eelwell Limestone, 8 m thick and easily distinguished by a prominent fauna of large *Gigantoproductus* brachiopods and corals including *Siphonodendron junceum*, develops small folds and minor associated thrusts throughout its foreshore outcrop. The limestone is locally dolomitized, brown weathering and vuggy. Just south of

Figure 3.4 West-facing overfold in the Eelwell Limestone, Saltpan Rocks (Locality 7). *Photo:* C. T. Scrutton.

Seahouse, it is involved in a sharp overfold facing west (Fig. 3.4), which further south is thrust through its short limb. On the top surfaces of the gentle, whaleback folds to the east and south, polished sections through the rich fauna of spiriferid brachiopods at the very top of the limestone can be seen. Out on the foreshore here the 30 cm Acre Coal occurs beneath sandstones showing medium–large scale lenticular cross-bedded sets. Where the coal crops out in the cliff at the back of the foreshore, it is involved in a small thrust with 1 m vertical displacement. Just above are excellent examples of climbing ripples and a rootlet bed. The 4.5 m thick Acre Limestone, also developing minor folds on the foreshore, has a very thin, impersistent sulphurous coal beneath it. The limestone, crinoidal, with scattered fossils and small algal nodules, is brown weathering, dolomitized and vuggy in the cliff.

The sequence of outcrops on the beach to the south, the Skerrs, are all formed of the 8.5 m thick Sandbanks Limestone, a series of thin limestone beds with shale partings. Near Skerr to Middle Skerr is a broad, shallow syncline and from Middle Skerr to Far Skerr a complementary anticline. Polished surfaces at Middle Skerr show excellent sections of *Zoophycos*. There are layers rich in brachiopods, and prominent solitary corals, mainly *Aulophyllum fungites* (with a dense axial structure) and rarer *Palaeosmilia murchisoni* (with many septa and no axial structure). In the sandstones below **trace fossils** are well seen; first the beaded burrow *Eione moniliforme* and then at lower levels, 10 cm long, dumbell-like depressions which are the bedding plane traces of the U-shaped burrow *Diplocraterion*. A careful search of joint surfaces may reveal vertical sections through the latter. Dark brown **chert** nodules occur towards the top of the limestone at Far Skerr; chert is characteristic of this limestone (=Four Fathom Limestone) across Northern England.

The next reef on the beach to the south is a thin, brown-weathering un-named limestone. Cheswick Black Rocks beyond, the last outcrop on the beach to the south, are formed of coarse, cross-bedded sandstones immediately beneath the Great Limestone. This limestone, known locally as the Dryburn, marks the base of the Upper Limestone Group and the Namurian (Upper Carboniferous). It was formerly quarried inland at Scremerston but it cannot now be seen on the shore.

4 · The Cheviot – early Devonian rocks, granite and basement

Peter Allen *British Geological Survey, Keyworth, Nottingham*

PURPOSE

To examine the rocks of the Cheviot volcano, including the basement beneath it, the **granite** and other intrusions, and the associated **hydrothermal** alteration and **metamorphism**.

LOGISTICS

There are two excursions, each comfortably done in a day. The first is along Harthope Burn, the second in Upper Coquet Dale. Both are primarily along roads suitable for minibuses, but with some localities up to 4 km away from the road.

Approach Harthope Burn either from Wooler or the A697 some 4 km south, following the signs to North Middleton. Access from Haugh Head on the A697 is not recommended because of a dangerous ford. Make for Middleton Hall, turning onto the single track road signposted to Langleeford. The road is mostly unfenced. It can be used only as far as Hawsen Burn (NT 95322252).

Reach upper Coquet Dale either from Alwinton (NT 92100630) or the A68 at Cottonshopeburn Foot (NT 78040157). From the A68 to Makendon (NT 80360932) is a military road and access may be barred when the artillery range is in use (check with the Army at Otterburn). For geological convenience this excursion, which is on unfenced, single track public road, is described from west to east.

Maps

O.S. 1:50 000 sheets 75 Berwick-upon-Tweed, 80 Cheviot Hills & Kielder Forest, 81 Alnwick & Morpeth; B.G.S. 1:50 000 Sheet 5 The Cheviot.

53

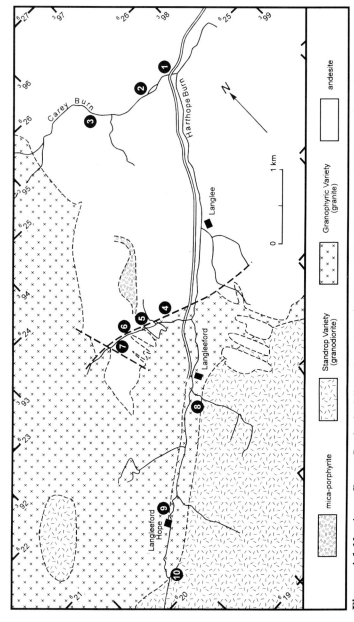

Figure 4.1 Harthope Burn. Geological lines from B.G.S. Sheet 5 The Cheviot and Jhingran (1943).

GEOLOGICAL BACKGROUND

The Cheviot volcano was erupted during the early Devonian period just to the north of the Iapetus **Suture**, the boundary between the Laurentian and Avalonian continents that marks the site of the Iapetus Ocean. The first outpourings of this subaerial volcano were of **agglomerate** and **breccia** which rest **unconformably** on a basement of **folded** sedimentary rocks of Silurian age, but most of the volcano consists of **andesite** lavas. **Rhyolite** lavas and thin interlayers of **tuff** are uncommon. Towards the end of its life granite was intruded into the central vent of the volcano. This is a zoned intrusion and, unusually for a granite, it contain the mineral **pyroxene**. There are many **dykes, sills** and **laccoliths**, which intruded the lava pile either while it was being built or soon after. The country rock adjacent to the granite was thermally metamorphosed during its emplacement, but also associated with it was a phase of intense hydrothermal alteration, locally involving the formation of the mineral **tourmaline**.

On the Scottish side, the volcanic rocks are overlain by Upper Devonian sandstones, but in Northumberland they are overlain by the Lower Carboniferous Cementstone Group, a cyclical sequence of sandy mudstone, shale, **cementstone, dolomitic** limestone and sandstone. **Basaltic** lavas occur at the base of the Carboniferous succession and within the Cementstone Group. In places, there is a basal Carboniferous **conglomerate** containing cobbles and boulders of andesite and granite. The latter indicates that much of the volcano, perhaps three quarters of it, had been eroded to unroof the granite intrusion before the conglomerate was laid down.

The Silurian sedimentary rocks forming the basement are tightly folded, but the lavas, though tilted gently to the east, are not folded. Many **faults** and shatter zones cross the volcanic terrain, including a major one along Harthope Burn, traced for 20 km.

The next major event in the area was the Quaternary glaciation. The hills were covered in ice during the late Devensian and remnant spreads of **till** are common. There are vast expanses of peat bog and head, immediately post glacial in origin. Alluvium and alluvial terraces occur in the valleys.

Rock exposure in the Cheviots is sparse, presenting severe problems for reconstructing the geological history. Thus it is important to accept that there may be other interpretations to those given here.

EXCURSION DETAILS

Harthope Burn

Locality 1, Careyburn Bridge (NT 97472501). Park on a grassy area just before the bridge and follow the footpath along the north side of Carey Burn. In the first 300 m three alluvial terraces are clearly seen on the north side. At the first style the small valley to the north cuts through till plastered against the lowest slopes of the hillside.

Locality 2 (NT 96982508) about 150 m upstream of the island in Carey Burn is the first exposure of solid rock. It is a dark purplish grey, splintery **porphyritic** andesite with small **phenocrysts** of white **feldspar** and dark pyroxene. The valley narrows just beyond here. There is plenty of rock on both sides, but the main rock types can be seen in the numerous screes along the path. Besides the dark purplish grey andesite, there is a common variety with big white feldspar phenocrysts (up to 1 cm long) and smaller pyroxene phenocrysts in a fine-grained reddish buff groundmass. The burn crosses the metamorphic aureole of the Cheviot granite and many of the rocks show signs of metamorphism. Feldspar phenocrysts are replaced by yellow **epidote** and the pyroxenes by pale green **tremolite** or dark green **chlorite**. There are often small crystals of black, flaky **biotite**. Spots of yellow epidote and patches of green chlorite occur in the groundmass.

Locality 3 (NT 96382553) is a waterfall in the burn. Solid rock is exposed for about 100 m below it. The geological map shows many dykes in this area. They are difficult to recognize and in the Geological Survey memoir the authors confess that sharp, intrusive contacts are rarely seen. The top of the waterfall consists of dark grey andesite, the bottom is a reddish buff fine-grained porphyritic rock, which may be one of the dykes. The contact between the two is not at all clear.

Locality 4, Hawsen Burn (NT 95322252). It is prohibited to drive beyond here. There is ample space for parking above and below the bridge and a turning area about 100 m beyond it. The burn runs along the contact between granite and country rock. Follow the stream itself, not the path parallel to it.

The first exposure is pink **microgranite** about 300 m up. A further 50 m beyond, a very small exposure in the stream shows a sharp contact between pink microgranite and dark purplish grey porphyritic andesite. This illustrates the nature of this contact, which is a complex series of dykes and veins of microgranite penetrating the andesite.

Locality 5 (NT 95012281) is 10 m beyond the first tributary coming in from the north. An exposure of andesite shows many features of contact metamorphism – close **joints**, splintery when struck, small dark spots in the groundmass. Upstream from here exposures of microgranite and andesite alternate.

Locality 6 (NT 94732296) is about 200 m below a circular, stone sheep fold. A big boulder of **quartz** with **haematite** stringers is in the stream adjacent to a breccia separating microgranite from rotted and quartz veined andesite. Veinlets of black tourmaline are in the microgranite. This locality marks the site of a west-northwest fault that is roughly coincident with the granite boundary.

Locality 7 (NT 94562302) is about 50 m below the sheepfold. A denuded patch of hillside, 3 m high, immediately above the stream is deeply hydrothermally altered, rotten andesite with 3 cm thick veins and stringers of tourmaline and lumps of massive epidote. This altered rock continues upstream adjacent to a crush zone first seen 100 m beyond the sheep fold. Two crush zones intersect here. A wall of breccia trending east–west stands at the foot of a steep slope which consists of crushed andesite up to 2 m wide with north–south quartz veins. Tourmaline, crystalline quartz, haematite and **limonite** are abundant. These crush zones are common in the Cheviots and are always associated with hydrothermal alteration.

Climb up to the footpath to return to the road. From there, the prominent Hausey and Long Crags on the east side of the Harthope valley to the southeast are roof pendants of **hornfelsed** volcanic rocks resting on granite. These, and a roof pendant of volcanic rocks actually on The Cheviot show that the exposed granite is the roof zone of the intrusion.

Walk along the road to Langleeford, then the track on the north side of the burn.

Locality 8 (NT 94502168). Near the edge of the wood on the north of the track is the first exposure of granite in the burn. It is pink and medium grained with pink feldspar, translucent quartz and black shiny flakes of biotite. There are 1 cm thick veins of sugary-textured **aplite** and 2–3 mm thick veinlets of black tourmaline. The granite intrusion has been divided into three main components arranged more or less concentrically. The Marginal Variety is not easy to access, but the Granophyric Variety of the next zone in is the one exposed here and for the next 2.5 km along the burn. It is a true granite in composition.

Locality 9 (NT 93332089) is at the gate across the track above Langleeford Hope. On both sides of the valley there is a spread of till. Looking south the spread ends where the hillside suddenly steepens. The till forms scarp faces along the burn, indented by landslides and their scars. This is the principle mechanism of erosion of the till sheet, the slipped material being dumped into the stream and carried away to be redeposited in the alluvial floodplain. A secondary process is solifluction, forming terrace-like features commonly described as sheep tracks. These are best seen upstream of the farm.

Locality 10 (NT 92792029) is the first waterfall in Harthope Burn. The contact between the Granophyric Variety and the Standrop Variety at the centre of the intrusion occurs in this area. Fine to medium-grained **granophyric** biotite granite occurs in the falls, containing areas of blotchy **porphyry** that have been described as volcanic **xenoliths**. Above the falls, near the stone sheep fold, the Standrop Variety appears. This is an even, medium-grained rock rich in dark minerals. Compositionally, it is a **granodiorite** and the commonest dark mineral is the pyroxene **diopside**. This rock continues upstream for some distance.

Upper Coquet Valley

Locality 1 (NT 80590952). Silurian basement is exposed at the bridge over the River Coquet about 350 m northeast of Makendon. Park at the bridge to traverse down-stream to Fulhope. A couple of metres below the bridge, in the left bank, is an **anticline** in interbedded greenish-grey silty mudstone with beds of fine sandstone up to 30 cm thick. The fold is open, upright and the axis trends 290°. A good, vertical axial plane **cleavage** is present in the silty mudstone, but not in the sandstone. A few metres upstream of the bridge, on the right bank, are several sandstone beds in silty mudstone. The sandstone units, up to 1 m thick, contain thin mudstone seams indicating they are composite beds. The medium to coarse-grained sandstone is composed of poorly sorted, subrounded to subangular grains of quartz, feldspar, rock fragments and dark minerals (?pyroxene), visible with a hand lens. Compositionally, it is typical of **greywackes**. Most of the greywacke beds here are massive (i.e. structureless), but some are faintly laminated and one or two show **flute casts** and load structures on the base indicating that the beds are the right way up. No fossils have been found here, but the rocks are thought to be Silurian in age.

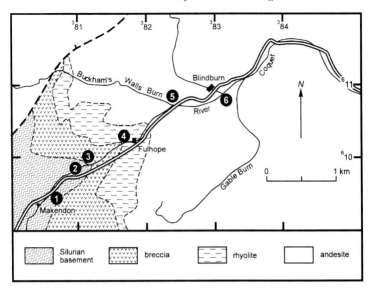

Figure 4.2 Upper Coquet Dale, around Blindburn. Geological lines from B.G.S. Sheet 5 The Cheviot.

Exposure continues downstream, the rocks striking roughly east–west and dipping steeply south. At intervals groups of several greywacke beds, 15–40 cm thick occur.

Locality 2 (NT 81000984) is a big meander after a long straight stretch. Thin beds of laminated greywacke in greenish-grey cleaved silty mudstone dip south at the first bend, but north at the second. Close examination will reveal a 4 cm thick dark sandy bed which has filled small channels scoured into the top of a paler grey laminated sandstone bed. The tops are to the south showing that these beds are overturned.

Locality 3 (NT 81110992). In a steep, rocky slope behind a wire fence above the stream is the base of the volcanic succession. The grassy slopes on the west contain debris of Silurian rocks. Clearly overlying these is a volcanic breccia, the first eruption of the Cheviot volcano. The base of the breccia and surfaces that appear to be bedding within it dip about 15° northeast, proving the unconformable relationship with the tightly folded Silurian basement rocks. The breccia is made

59

up of rubbly angular to subangular **clasts**, mostly of acid volcanic rocks from a few cm in diameter to over 1 m, set in a very fine-grained pink recrystallized clastic matrix. A careful search will reveal some Silurian clasts in the breccia. This lowermost unit in the volcanic pile is 30 to 60 m thick hereabouts.

Locality 4 (NT 81671017). About 200 m above Fulhope, is an exposure of deep purple rhyolite (or mica-felsite) with small phenocrysts of white feldspar and less common black biotite. The rock is severely altered to limonite. A prominent subhorizontal platy jointing, 1–3 cm apart, is sometimes filled with quartz veinlets. This is a primary feature caused during cooling of the lava flow. The rock weathers dark grey. Looking back, a line of small exposures of it can be seen at the base of a step feature that can be traced for several hundred metres west, overlying another step feature formed by the basal breccia.

Locality 5 (NT 82401078) is an old, small quarry at the start of the path along Buckham's Walls Burn. Park on an area of hard standing near the bridge. The rock is typical andesite, dark purplish grey with large white feldspar and small pyroxene phenocrysts, and clots of dark minerals. It is a massive, structureless rock, but it is closely jointed. The joints are planar on the west but curved, convex to the southeast, on the east. This phenomenon often occurs parallel to the base or sides of a flow.

Locality 6 (NT 83071087) is in the stream opposite the houses at Blindburn. In the waterfall just downstream of the houses and in exposures upstream is volcanic breccia. The rock consists of matrix-supported angular to subangular clasts, mostly of green andesite up to several tens of cm in diameter. The matrix is greenish grey, fine grained and full of small, irregular shaped, chlorite-filled **amygdales**. Rock the same as the matrix occurs alternating with exposures of deep purple andesite downstream to the junction with Gable Burn (NT 83421105). Units of breccia and finer-grained tuffs occur throughout the andesite pile. They have not been studied in recent years. At Blindburn the textures visible in outcrop suggest the rock might be a **pyroclastic** flow breccia rather than an air-fall deposit.

Locality 7 (NT 89190649), at Linbriggs, is the best of the many exposures of andesite in the river. Park near the farm buildings and start with the roadside exposure on the east side, about 30 m south of the bridge. At the southern end of the exposure is massive, purplish

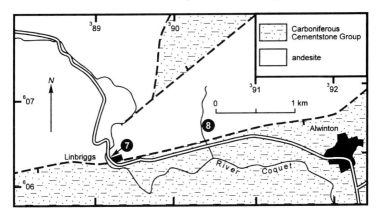

Figure 4.3 Upper Coquet Dale, near Alwinton. Geological lines from B.G.S. Sheet 5 The Cheviot.

grey porphyritic andesite, which passes northwards into finely brecciated, amygdaloidal rock marking the top of the flow. Above and to the north is a second flow of rubbly andesite. This rock is purplish brown and highly amygdaloidal with epidote and chlorite-filled irregular vesicles. Blocks and 'pillows' are set in hydrothermally altered, rotted andesite, but the flow has a core of massive rock some 6 m long and 2.5 m high. In the gorge, upstream of the bridge, the general southerly dip to the pile of flows is clearly seen. Good, polished exposures of amygdaloidal and flow-banded andesite are present in the river bed.

Locality 8 (NT 90400648) is a cattle grid 1.5 km beyond Alwinton. The southern boundary of the Cheviot Volcanic Group is faulted. The road from here to Linbriggs is close to and parallel to the fault. Small craggy exposures in the steep hillside on the north of the road are andesite. On the southern side of the Coquet valley, on Barrow Scar, subhorizontal, well-bedded Carboniferous rocks are clearly visible (Excursion 9). Note at the eastern end of the exposure the prominent upper limestone bed has sagged as a result of landslipping. The fault can be positioned to within a metre in the stream running down to the road here from the north. Here, about 50 m from the road, a small exposure of sandstone is a metre from andesite.

5 · The Lower Carboniferous of Bewcastle and Gilsland

Mark Purnell *University of Leicester* and
Howard Armstrong *University of Durham*

PURPOSE

The excursion describes the Lower Carboniferous rocks of the Northumberland-Cumbria border country around Bewcastle and along the River Irthing.

LOGISTICS

The itinerary (Fig. 5.1) has been chosen to be easily accessible, and to be completed by car or minibus in one day; only Locality 4 is suitable for large parties. Refreshment and toilet facilities are available at Gilsland and in various pubs.

Note: Permission for access to Birky Cleugh (Locality 2) should be sought in advance from the Forest District Manager, Kielder Forest District, Eals Burn, Bellingham, Hexham, Northumberland (Tel: 01434 220242).

Maps

O.S. 1:50 000 Sheet 86 Haltwhistle, Bewcastle & Alston; B.G.S. 1:63 360 Sheet 12 Bewcastle (solid and drift editions).

GEOLOGICAL BACKGROUND

The area covered comprises a mixture of rolling agricultural land and peat covered moorland rising to 500 m above sea level. It is dominated geologically by Carboniferous sandstones, marine limestones and shales of the Lower, Middle and Upper Border groups, and the Liddesdale Group (Fig. 5.1). These are **unconformably** overlain by Permian basal **breccias** and shales, and a thick blanket of glacial deposits.

The Carboniferous rocks of the area were deposited in a shallow trough bordered to the north by the subdued **Caledonian** Mountains of the Southern Uplands and, to the south, by the Alston Block. These upstanding margins of the trough were sources of **clastic** sediment during Lower Border Group times, but large drainage systems from the north and east dominated deposition through much of the later Carboniferous. At times of high clastic sediment input or lower sea level, extensive deltas, sometimes topped by coal-forming swamps, **prograded** into the shallow gulf-like sea which occupied the trough in this area. Periodically, reduced sediment supply or higher sea level led to northeastward **transgression** of marine conditions. Thus the sandstones, shales and limestones of the Lower and Upper Border groups encountered at the localities detailed below reflect the complex interplay of these fluviodeltaic and marine depositional systems.

During deposition of the Liddesdale Group fully marine conditions dominated the area. The Southern Uplands and Alson Block, until this time the margins to the basin, were finally breached by the sea and limestone was laid down in laterally persistent beds, some of which extended north into the Midland Valley of Scotland and south into Yorkshire. In mid-Carboniferous time thick sands prograded from the northeast (Millstone Grit). The late Carboniferous saw the development of swamp conditions and deposition of the Coal Measures. Regional **tectonic** compression during the late Carboniferous and early Permian resulted in uplift and prolonged subaerial erosion. The late Permian transgression, from the south, deposited the St. Bees and Kirklington sandstones, widely used in local buildings.

The present drainage systems were established during Tertiary uplift. Pleistocene glacial advance and retreat covered the area in thick **till**, overlain by sands and gravels, but in Holocene times the major rivers have re-located in their pre-glacial courses. Post-glacial climates favoured the formation of an extensive upland peat blanket.

More recent history is also of considerable interest. There are scattered signs of ancient British settlements throughout the area, and from about 120 A.D. Bewcastle was the site of the Roman fort of *Banna*. After Roman occupation the fort became an Anglo-Saxon settlement and a well preserved, carved sandstone cross, now located in the churchyard, dates from this period. Subsequent Norse occupation, for a time under the chieftain Beuth, gave Bewcastle its name. The church and castle which now stand on the site of the fort were built during the reign of Edward I in about 1291. The castle was destroyed by Cromwell's troops in 1641.

Further details of the geology can be found in Day (1970).

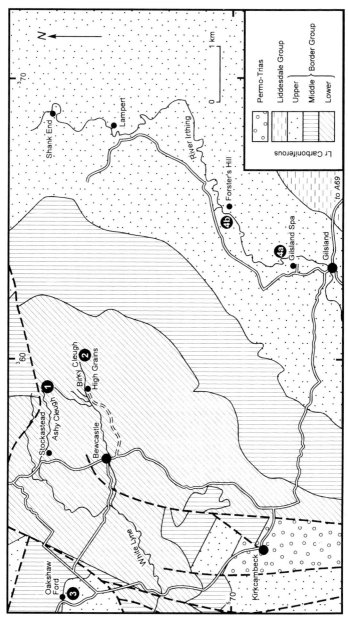

Figure 5.1 General geological map of the Gilsland–Bewcastle area showing localities described in the text.

EXCURSION DETAILS

Locality 1, Ashy Cleugh (NY 565770 – 570767; Fig. 5.2). Permission for access should be sought from Stockastead Farm. Park by the track, near the disused limekiln.

Locality 1a (NY 565770). Here the stream exposes the uppermost Lynebank Formation and the Bewcastle Formation. The lowermost unit of the latter, the 11 m thick Bogside Limestone Member, forms a series of small waterfalls and in the past has been quarried from this locality for lime. The Bogside Limestone is one of the thickest limestones developed in either the Lower Border or Cementstone groups over the area covered by this guide. It was deposited below normal wave base in a shallow marine environment. Thin bands packed with fossils were formed when occasional storms stirred up the sea floor and winnowed out the shelly material in the muddy sediment. The fossil fauna is dominated by **brachiopods** (mainly *Antiquatonia teres*), brachiopod spines, and **crinoid** fragments. The thin shale horizon towards the middle of the unit contains a moderately diverse **bivalve** fauna.

Above the Bogside Limestone, shales with occasional sandstones and thin limestones, some of which are marine, crop out in the stream bed and banks (Fig. 5.2). The persistent can reach Ashy Cleugh Locality 1b by following the stream through the trees.

Locality 1b. From the limekiln, walk up around the south side of the quarry and along the edge of the small conifer plantation. Upstream from the edge of the plantation (NY 570767) the upper part of the Bewcastle Formation, from the New House Limestone Member to the Junction Limestone Member (Fig. 5.2), is exposed in the stream bed and in a series of low, shaley bluffs. This part of the formation is dominated by shales, with only a few sandstone and limestone beds, most of which are less than 1 m in thickness. Some of the shales are brecciated and probably represent the collapsed remains of **evaporite** beds, now leached away. Marine fossils are uncommon except in the 2.6 m thick Ashy Cleugh Limestone Member; its fauna is similar to that of the Bogside Limestone Member, although rather impoverished, and it was probably deposited in a similar environment. Occasional thin beds of **oolite** indicate high energy marine conditions, but the general absence of fully marine fossils from this part of the Bewcastle Formation, and the more common occurrences of bivalves, including *Modiolus*, **ostracodes**, vermiform '**gastropods**',

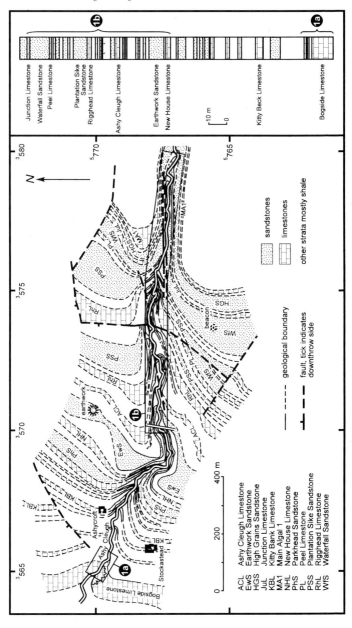

Figure 5.2 Geological map and section exposed in Ashy Cleugh (based on Day 1970, figs. 8(8), 9).

algae, and abundant fragmentary plant remains suggest that marine influence was limited at this time.

Locality 2, Birky Cleugh (NY 588754 – 593754; Fig. 5.3). Birky Cleugh is an **S.S.S.I.** and prior permission for access should be sought (see Logistics); *hammering is not permitted* but loose fossils may be collected. From Bewcastle church, take the road over the river past the Limekiln Inn. After 200 m go through the gate by the post-box on the left and take the right-hand track for about 2.5 km to High Grains House; park by the track. *Note:* The track to High Grains can be muddy and is very rough in places.

In the shallow gorge below the house the High Grains Sandstone Member of the uppermost Bewcastle Formation can be seen. Walk round the north side of the house and take the track down to the stream. Upstream from the point where the track crosses Birky Cleugh (NY 588754) the whole of the Main Algal Formation and the lower part of the overlying Cambeck Formation is exposed as a series of low bluffs and waterfalls. The prominent orange weathering limestone in the first bluff is Main Algal Limestone Member 1 (Fig. 5.3), which contains small but well developed algal-vermiform 'gastropod' patch reefs. The thick limestone in the waterfall 150 m upstream is the Birky Cleugh Limestone Member. Most of the limestones of the Main Algal Formation are algal in character and well developed algal nodules and encrusting mats are exposed at various horizons in Birky Cleugh. At the time of their deposition this area was a warm, shallow marine gulf with fluctuating salinity and minimal tidal activity. The lower parts of the Cambeck Formation exposed in the higher reaches of the stream (Fig. 5.3) contain a more fully marine shelly fauna dominated by the brachiopod *Antiquatonia teres*.

Locality 3, River Black Lyne – Oakshaw Ford (NY 513766). Permission for access must be sought from Mr Drew at Clattering Ford cottage. This site is scheduled to become an S.S.S.I. so *outcrops should not be hammered*. The track down to the river passes made ground on the left. This is the remains of workings for the Oakshaw Coal. Though of poor quality and high ash content this was worked from the 19th Century to the late 1940s as a source of household fuel. On the south bank of the river a number of small quarries expose the Oakshaw Limestone. At the top of the limestone a thin bed of volcanic **tuff** (highly weathered to clay) is thought to be a much attenuated representative of the Glencartholm Volcanic Beds found further north

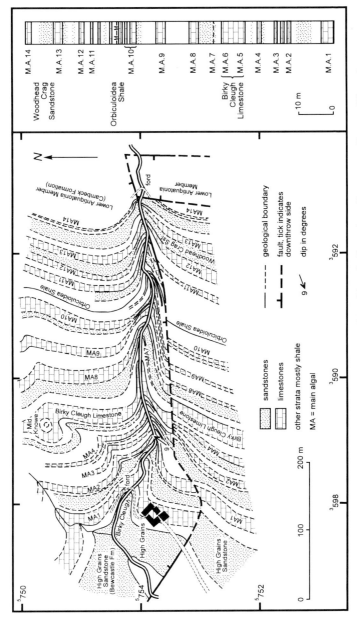

Figure 5.3 Geological map and section exposed in Birky Cleugh (based on Day 1970, figs. 13(6), 15).

in the Scottish borders. The 'Clattering Band', lies about 1 m below the Oakshaw Limestone and though now partially overgrown, is exposed on the opposite bank of the river. The Clattering Band is taken as the base of the Upper Border Group in the Bewcastle area and contains a shelly fauna originally described by Garwood. This includes colonies of the **corals** *Lithostrotion portlocki* and *Siphonodendron martini* in growth position. The brachiopods *Punctospirifer scabricosta* and *Stenoscisma isorhyncha* are also common.

Locality 4, Irthing Gorge. The Upper Border Group rocks to the north of Gilsland form part of the gently dipping eastern limb of the Bewcastle **Anticline**. A succession extending from below the Miller-hill Limestone to above the Leahill Limestone is well exposed in the River Irthing between Gilsland and Shankend (NY 68777654). This section is repeatedly cut by **faults** of the Gilsland Fault Belt. *Some of these localities are on M.O.D. land; heed the warnings posted along the road.*

Locality 4A, Gilsland Gorge (NY 635680). Though the sections in the gorge are largely inaccessible they allow the opportunity to view the dominantly **arenaceous**, middle part of the Upper Border Group. Descend the steep path to the north of the car park of the Gilsland Spa Hotel. Follow signs to the Popping Stone, crossing two suspension bridges. The development of the gorge is controlled by a series of northwest **striking**, normal faults. The lowest exposed beds comprise calcareous sandstones (NY 63506904), overlain by approximately 35 m of mainly arenaceous strata. A sequence of Crammel Linn, Green Grove and Collering Sandstones is exposed along the northern side of the gorge, where individual beds show marked lateral thickness variation. In the section west of the Popping Stone (NY 63506812) the upper part of the Crammel Linn Sandstone is almost entirely replaced by shales.

Locality 4B, West of Forster's Hill (NY 65257030). From the road (NY 64187060) follow the deep gully of the unnamed burn southeast-wards to the River Irthing. At the confluence, a series of isolated outcrops expose the 2 m thick, shale dominated sequence which lies below the Spy Rigg Sandstone. The Throssburnfoot Coal can be found about 1 m below the sandstone. Shales beneath the coal contain an abundant fauna including the freshwater bivalve *Naidites obesus* and primitive **mollusc** *Bellerophon* sp. This level represents the locally developed 'Irthing Shell Bed'. Thin calcareous shales within the section yield occasional brachiopods, gastropods and **nautiloids**.

In cliff exposures 100 m further downstream, (NY 65157020) a pair of Tertiary, **tholeiitic dykes** 1–2 m thick incline to the southwest. Shales to the south are baked and **cleaved**. In the cliff a thin coal becomes anthracitic and cindery close to the intrusion. At 1–1.5 m from the southern contact and parallel to it are bands of brecciated and decomposed **dolerite**. Occasional vesicles up to 0.5 mm in diameter are filled with clay minerals. The Spy Rigg Sandstone is well developed in the opposite bank where it is affected by a series of small faults.

6 · Geology and landscape of Holy Island and Bamburgh

Bert Randall *formerly University of Newcastle upon Tyne*
and **John Senior** *University of Durham*

PURPOSE

A two-part excursion to examine the geology and landscape of Holy
Island (Lindisfarne) and the Whin Sill near Bamburgh.

LOGISTICS

On Holy Island, the official car park is on the northeast side of the
village (NU 128421, Fig. 6.1a). At Bamburgh, parking is often
possible on the grass at the side of The Wynding; otherwise use the car
park opposite Bamburgh Castle (NU 183348, Fig. 6.5). Holy Island
lies within the Lindisfarne National Nature Reserve, so the use of
hammers is forbidden without the permission of English Nature (Tel:
0191 281 6316).

Note: Holy Island is cut off from the mainland at high tide. Tide and
recommended crossing times are posted at the mainland end of the
causeway to the island. Towards high tide the surge channel (the
Lindis Beck) fills very rapidly and unwary travellers and their cars are
regularly inundated by the sea! Do this part of the excursion on a
falling tide.

Maps

O.S. 1:50 000 Sheet 75, Berwick-upon-Tweed; O.S. 1:25 000 Sheet 452
(NU 04/14), Holy Island; B.G.S. 1:50 000 Sheet 4, Holy Island
(solid); 1:63 360 Sheet 4, Holy Island (drift).

GEOLOGICAL BACKGROUND

The rock head geology of Holy Island consists of a near peneplaned
surface of cyclic sediments belonging to the Lower Carboniferous,

71

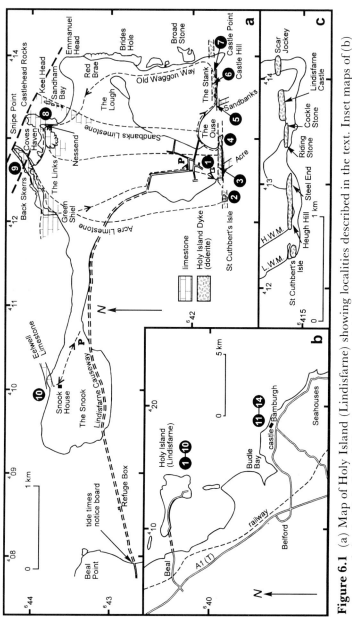

Figure 6.1 (a) Map of Holy Island (Lindisfarne) showing localities described in the text. Inset maps of (b) access roads in the Holy Island/Bamburgh area, and (c) of the Holy Island dyke echelon segments.

Middle Limestone Group (Brigantian Stage). Each cycle starts with fossiliferous marine limestone (Eelwell, Acre and Sandbanks), followed normally by marine shales then deltaic sediments including non-marine shales with ironstone **concretions**, siltstones, sandstones, a **seatearth** and thin coal.

During the **Variscan Orogeny** these Carboniferous sediments were subject to east–west compression against the Cheviot Block. The resulting shear force produced a series of minor **anticlines** and **synclines**, particularly well exposed along the northern shore of Holy Island, and also allowed the emplacement of the Holy Island **Dyke**. This is the most northerly of the four late-Carboniferous **doleritic** dyke **echelons** of the north of England which belong to the Whin **Sill** suite. The off-set nature of the Holy Island Dyke echelon results in a series of low islands (St Cuthbert's Isle, Plough Rock, Plough Seat, Goldstone Rock) and low hills (Heugh Hill and Beblowe (Castle) Hill).

The individual dyke segments are topographically highest at their western ends and their upper surfaces are characterized by flat planes gently dipping to the east. These surfaces are formed of chilled rock and indicate that the dyke 'topped', i.e. reached an upward termination below the erosion surface at the time of intrusion (Randall & Farmer, 1970). A 150–230 mm zone a few centimetres below the chilled surface contains numerous **amygdales**, up to 406 × 203 by 25 mm deep, which are markedly flattened, parallel to the chilled surface (indicating the easterly **dip** to be **tectonic**) and elongated in locally consistent directions between northeast and southeast. The amygdales contain **quartz** and **calcite** but where the filling has been removed, the lower surface exhibits ropy flow structures analogous to those on lava flow surfaces.

The Whin Sill was intruded penecontemporaneously with the dykes and although around Bamburgh it is not as thick as in County Durham it displays fascinating intrusive relationships.

Late Quaternary glaciers left a patchy cover of **tills** containing **erratics** of local, Cheviot and Scottish origin (Hodgson *in* Fullerton & Sharp, 1980). After the last, Devensian, glaciation sea-level was much lower in the North Sea Basin, and in Mesolithic times (8500–6500 B.C.) Holy Island was a low hill on a wide coastal plain with the coast-line at about -30 m. Rising sea-level at the end of the Mesolithic period (6500–3000 B.C.) destroyed the land bridge between Eastern England and Netherlands/Denmark and flooded the coastal plains of north Northumberland. Mesolithic flint scatters and 9th century A.D. farm settlements found at the base of the sand dune cover which occurs over much of the northern part of the island suggests that these dune sands (The Links and The Snook) are of recent origin.

EXCURSION DETAILS

Holy Island

Locality 1, Priory and Parish Church (NU 126417). From the village car park (Fig. 6.1a, NU 128421) walk to the largely 13th century Benedictine Priory and St Mary's parish church (13th century with later additions). Note the handsome red sandstone ashlar used in the Priory church which is reputed to have been brought from mainland shoreline quarries at Cheswick Black Rocks (NU 038477), but could equally have been quarried from the eastern shore line of the island. The purple, reddish and white sandstones used in the parish church were certainly obtained from the Nessend area (Locality 8, NU 131438); much dolerite from The Heugh has been used as the rubble core of the walls. All the sandstone ashlar has been weathered to some extent by the prevailing wind and rain. Particularly fine examples of deep reticulate weathering may be seen on the crossing piers in the Priory church.

Locality 2, St Cuthbert's Island or Hobthrush (NU 123416). This low island southwest of the parish church is only accessible at low water. No vertical contacts are exposed on the eastern margin of this segment of the dyke echelon, but the dominant **joints** on the island are sub-horizontal. The flat surface, which has a slight easterly dip, and which lies mainly below high water mark, is formed of chilled rock (Fig. 6.2a). The lower amygdale zone can be traced in the low cliffs on the north and west shores of the island. On the east side there is a marked feature formed by a minor normal north–south **fault** zone (down-throwing c. 1 m to the east) which repeats the dyke sequence.

The remains of a hermitage used by St Cuthbert around 685 AD are still visible.

Locality 3 (NU 126416). The contact between the dyke and the Carboniferous country rock is particularly well exposed along the southern margin of the Heugh Hill dyke segment. About 60 m from the western end, there are three small rafts of saccharoidal limestone in the southern contact zone and a little to the east 'skins' of limestone indicate that much of the lower part of the exposure is actual dyke wall. The dominant cooling joints are near vertical and perpendicular

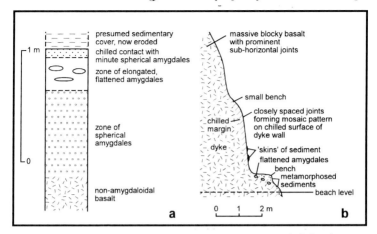

Figure 6.2 (a) Section of top of dyke on St Cuthbert's Island (Locality 2). (b) Profile of southern wall of the Heugh Hill dyke segment (Locality 3).

to the dyke wall, but obvious jointing also occurs parallel to the dyke wall.

The Acre Limestone is exposed on the foreshore 200 m to the east (NU 127416). The limestone is quite fossiliferous with many small productid **brachiopods**, spiriferids and occasional small orthoconic **nautiloids**. Generally it is flat lying but here it has been flexed into a number of northerly elongated dome-like structures. Further east on the foreshore, just beyond the path over Heugh Hill, the shale overlying the limestone has been notably bleached and spotted (**metamorphosed**). Just to the east of the path a **xenolith** of shale can be seen in the dyke.

On clear days there are fine views of the Farne Islands (east-southeast), Bamburgh Castle (south) and the Kyloe Hills with the Cheviot Hills in the distance (southwest) from the coastguard building (NU 127417). Geophysical surveys on the Heugh revealed the foundation of several buildings on the crest of this dyke segment, including rectangular remains possibly of the Anglo-Scandinavian monastic watch tower, the likely base of a windmill (the 'Cockpit') and the late 17th century Fort overlooking Steel End.

On the foreshore some 75 m east of the path, a near horizontal surface or bench, c.1.5 m wide and just above beach level, occurs in the southern wall of the dyke (Fig. 6.2b). There are patchy skins of

75

sediments on both the dyke wall, visible to a height of 6 m, and the bench, which extends eastwards for 75 m.

Locality 4, Steel End (NU 130416). At the eastern end of the Heugh Hill dyke segment, a smooth chilled surface dipping 5° east, exposed at low tide, represents the original upper surface of the dyke. Abundant elongate amygdales and many 'ropy flow' structures, all with a southwest trend, can be seen where not seaweed covered. To the west are a series of northwest–southeast trending shatter zones.

The Ouse embayment, viewed from the jetty at Steel End, originated by the erosion of softer Carboniferous sediments, and is protected to the west and east by sections of the Holy Island Dyke (The Heugh and Riding Stone). Walking east around The Ouse note the depression between the shingle ridge on the west side of the bay and the priory ruins, the residue of a seaward extension of the channel from The Lough.

Locality 5, Cockle Stone (NU 134417). Near the wooden remains of the lime jetty at high water mark on the eastern side of The Ouse are exposures of the Sandbanks Limestone with small brachiopods

Figure 6.3 Bench on the Cockle Stone segment of the Holy Island Dyke, with Lindisfarne Castle on the Castle Hill segment in the background. *Photo:* C. T. Scrutton.

(productids, spiriferids and *Chonetes*), intruded by the Riding Stone-Cockle Stone segment of the dyke echelon. At the south side of the eastern end of the segment a 4 m wide flat bench of chilled rock (Fig. 6.3) exhibits 'ropy flow' structures which trend east-northeast.

Locality 6, Castle or Beblowe Hill (NU 136418). From this high vantage point on the southeast side of the island, the southward-staggered emplacement of segments of the Holy Island Dyke echelon (Plough Rock, Castle Hill, Riding Stone, the Heugh and St Cuthbert's Isle) is clear, and is reflected in the off-set nature of the coastline to the west. The boggy hollow to the north of the castle with the large pool ('The Stank') is all that remains of a marine gulf that once separated the Castle Hill island from the rest of Holy Island. This gulf is now partly filled with marine sediments.

Here the dyke segment is almost 60 m wide. At the western end, skins of sediments cling to the south wall of the dyke which dips 60° south. Below the castle a small 'white Whin' off-shoot from the main dyke extends some 11.5 m into shale. Joints parallel to the dyke wall are obvious along the length of the dyke, but near the lime kilns these joints flatten giving the false impression that the dyke is converting into a sill.

Locality 7, Castle Point Lime Kilns (NU 138417). At the eastern end of Castle Hill is the large complex of six limekilns built in 1860. Large quantities of limestone (for example, 3590 tons for the year ending October 1866), brought from Nessend Quarry (NU 130438) via the mineral waggonway (now used as a pathway), were calcined in these kilns. The lime was shipped from the Castle Jetty.

Follow the path north along the old limestone waggonway past The Lough, a freshwater body of 9th century origin, presumably constructed during the monastic development.

Locality 8, Nessend (NU 130438). East from Nessend, the rocky skerries of Keel Head divide Sandham Bay into two unequal parts. These harder rocks are the upper **posts** of the Sandbanks Limestone, sandwiched between two shale units which are eroded away to form the main bay feature. The lower units of the Sandbanks Limestone formerly formed the cap rock of Nessend, but the hard yellowish limestone was exploited during the 19th century to provide feedstock for the limekilns at Castle Point. These limestones are remarkably unfossiliferous.

The 20 m vertical cliffs (beware of falling rocks and nesting birds)

Figure 6.4 Cliff on northwest side of Nessend (Locality 8) showing sequence below capping of Sandbanks Limestone (with nesting birds). *Photo:* J. R. Senior.

forming the northwest coast of Nessend overlooking Coves Haven (NU 131439), are capped by a Sandbanks Limestone selvage left by quarrying (Fig. 6.4). Beneath the limestone is an excellent section in the Acre Limestone Cyclothem; shales with ironstone **concretions** (at beach level) overlain by thin flaggy sandstones and then thicker units of sandstone which show signs of hand working for building stone (possibly mediaeval) and black powder blasting (19th century). The colours of the sandstones *in situ* (white, reddish and purples) match those of the sandstone ashlar used in the village and Parish Church. Towards the top of this cliff is a prominent impure coal horizon.

Continue northwest across Coves Haven, an embayment produced by the erosion of softer shales. Around 1790 ironstone nodules from the shales were mined in the intertidal area by the Carron (Iron) Company and exported by sea to feed smelters at Falkirk.

Locality 9, Snipe Point and Back Skerrs (NU 126440–123439). Here at low tide, an erosion surface of easterly dipping Acre Limestone shows a splendid complex of shallow north–south **periclines** and basins east of Snipe Point (NU 127441) and at Back Skerrs (NU 123439), an effect of the Ford-Felkington Disturbance Zone. The eastern end of Snipe

Point promontory is truncated diagonally by a west-northwest–east-southeast wrench fault which continues across the mouth of Coves Haven to Castlehead; a smaller parallel wrench fault with associated **calcite**-filled tension gashes and **slickensiding** on Snipe Point promontory can be seen to truncate and therefore post-date the pericline-basin complex.

The Acre Limestone at Snipe Point, which contains small productid brachiopods, zaphrentid **corals** and **trace fossils**, is overlain by thin shales and siltstones with **sideritic** concretions. North from Snipe Point, the base of the limestone is underlain in places by vestigial coals, seatearth and sandstones with sideritic concretions.

Continue to the 9th century settlement site at Green Shiel, turn south past deteriorating kilns of the Kennedy Limeworks (c. 1850) and join the western waggonway which leads back towards the village and the carpark.

Locality 10, The Snook (NU 100437). Should time and tides permit, park off the road at the Lindisfarne Causeway and Jack Mathison's Bank junction (NU 107434) and walk northwest towards Snook House. On the coast to the north the **dolomitized** and flexured Eelwell Limestone is exposed, containing the compound coral *Actinocyathus floriformis* and brachiopods. This limestone was worked for lime burning in the 1790s and calcined in a one pot kiln on site (no longer visible) using local coals for fuel.

Bamburgh

Drive to Bamburgh and park either in the car park or at the side of The Wynding (Fig. 6.5).

Locality 11, Bamburgh Castle (NU 183351). In the crag below the castle the Whin Sill is **transgressive** across the cross-bedded, red Carboniferous sandstone, rising from northeast to southwest.

Locality 12, Harkess Rocks (NU 177356). Here the upper chilled margin of the Whin Sill is well exposed on the foreshore close to the base of the small cliff. Just below the chilled contact are numerous elongated amygdales (of a similar nature to those seen in the Holy Island Dyke), indicating that this upper contact was horizontal during sill emplacement. The amygdales can often be measured in metres, are often filled with quartz and calcite with a little **chlorite**, and frequently have ropy-flow structures, the latter indicating an

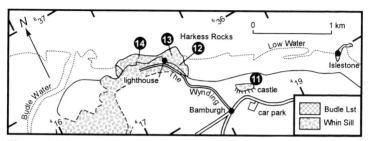

Figure 6.5 Map of localities in the Bamburgh area.

east–west flow direction. A few inclusions of limestone and shale are visible close to the contact.

To the northwest the sill is covered by sand, but reappears at a higher level as a 1.50 m fault scarp, perpendicular to the coastline, in which inclusions of shale can be seen. Towards the sea, the sill transgresses up through shale along a north–south line; this exposure is terminated by a fracture zone with several splay faults trending east-northeast. A second complex fracture zone occurs some 20–30 m further northwest, with the dips of coarse sandstones changing from 35° east to 20° northwest across the fault zone.

Locality 13, Stag Rock (NU 175358). This almost vertical exposure, trending almost due east, is ornamented by the painted figure of a stag. Adjacent to the lighthouse the Whin Sill has been injected into shale above the Budle Limestone, but halfway to Stag Rock the sill has transgressed into shales underlying the limestone, which is now on the dip slope above the sill. Further out towards the sea the Budle Limestone is again found below the sill. Northwest of the lighthouse the limestone, in an anticline, again rests on the sill.

Locality 14, (NU 172360). Here the sill contains a large basin-shaped limestone inclusion some 1.5 thick and 20 m in diameter, whilst 300 m further west (NU 171360), the Whin Sill and the overlying limestone have been polished and etched by wind-blown sand.

7 · Carboniferous rocks of the Howick shore section

Maurice Tucker *University of Durham*

PURPOSE

The excursion will examine rocks of the Carboniferous Limestone Groups and the Whin **Sill** on the Northumberland coast near Howick, from Longhoughton Steel in the south to Cullernose Point in the north.

LOGISTICS

The rocks are described from south to north. Park near Low Stead Farm (NU 262157), 2 km east-northeast of Longhoughton. Parking is also available 3 km farther north along the road near Cullernose Point (NU 259182). Although some exposures can still be seen at high tide, it is best to visit the coast from mid to low tide.

Maps

O.S. 1:50 000 Sheet 81, Alnwick & Morpeth; B.G.S. 1:50 000 Sheet 6 Alnwick (solid and drift editions).

GEOLOGICAL BACKGROUND

Carboniferous sediments of northern England were deposited in the east-northeast–west-southwest-trending Northumberland Trough, a broad **half-graben** structure divided into the Northumberland, Solway and Tweed basins. To the north was located the emergent Southern Uplands Block, and to the south, across the Ninety Fathom-Stublick **Fault** system, the more slowly subsiding Alston Block. The early Dinantian, basin-fill sediments were deposited at a time of extension when the southern boundary fault system was active. Later sediments (Namurian and Westphalian) were deposited more uniformly over the whole northern England area as a result of regional subsidence. The deposits of the Northumberland Trough consist chiefly of sandstones and mudrocks with subordinate limestones and coals. Palaeocurrent and provenance studies indicate that on a broad scale the **siliciclastic** sediments were sourced from a large catchment area to the north and east, whereas more open-marine environments were located to the south and west.

The Carboniferous succession of eastern Northumberland is divided into eight stratigraphic units: the Cementstone Group, Fell Sandstone Group, Scremerston Coal Group, Lower, Middle and Upper Limestone Groups, Millstone Grit and Coal Measures. The sediments of the Limestone Groups (up to 1000 m thick) are markedly rhythmic, consisting of some 25 '**Yoredale**' cycles, ranging from 20–100 m in thickness. Typically these begin with a thin, dark, marine shale below a muddy, **micritic bioclastic** limestone which may reach several metres in thickness. The latter is overlain by dark shales which coarsen up into rippled and **cross-bedded** sandstones. In some cycles there is a channelized sandstone up to 10 m thick, cutting down into the coarsening-upward siliciclastic unit. The cycle is capped by a variety of **palaeosols**, including **seatearths, ganisters** and thick coals. Much thinner coarsening-upward siliciclastic units on the scale of a few metres or less, capped by a thin palaeosol, may occur above the main coarsening-upward cycle before the black shale and limestone of the succeeding cycle. Each cycle is generally named after the limestone at its base.

These 'Yoredale' cycles are interpreted as the product of flooding of a delta plain (deposition of the thin marine shale) where the palaeosols were developing (thicker coals), followed by carbonate deposition in an open-marine environment, before the gradual advance of a deltaic shoreline and the deposition of the major coarsening-upward silici-clastic unit. The channelized sandstone represents the fluvial dis-tributary which supplied the sediment to the delta front. The small-scale coarsening-upward units at the top of a cycle represent local flooding of the lower delta plain and the infilling of interdistributary bays, lagoons and lakes.

Sediments of the Namurian Upper Limestone Group are exposed from Howdiemont Bay in the south to Howick Bay in the north (Figs. 7.1, 7.2). There is a major east–west fault in Howick Bay to the north of which are sediments of the Lower Carboniferous (Dinantian) Middle Limestone Group. Some 200 m of intervening strata, includ-ing the Great Limestone, are not exposed (Farmer and Jones, 1969). The regional **dip** is at a low angle to the east, reflecting the broad

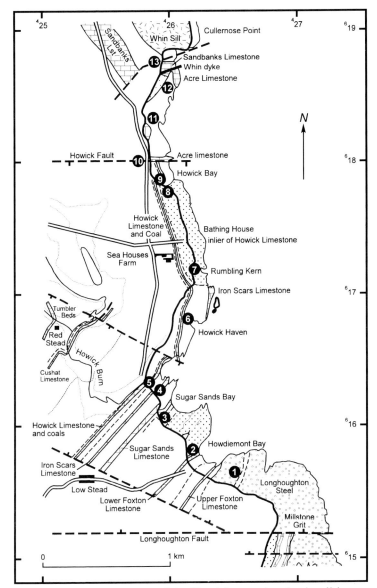

Figure 7.1 Geological map of the Howick area showing localities mentioned in the text.

concentric pattern of Carboniferous rocks in Northumberland dipping away from the Devonian lavas and **granite** of the Cheviot Hills. Locally there are variations in this pattern and small **folds** are present.

EXCURSION DETAILS

Locality 1 (NU 265156). From the cliff-top car park near Low Stead Farm walk eastwards along the beach to the foreshore outcrops at Longhoughton Steel. These are sediments of the 'Millstone Grit' of Namurian (Kinderscoutian) age: coarse pebbly sandstones with well-developed cross-bedding separated from the underlying finer-grained sandstones of the Upper Limestone Group by a sharp erosion surface. The 'Millstone Grit' represents a major fluvial system transporting coarse clastic sediments towards the south/southwest.

Locality 2 (NU 262158). Walk northwestwards across the sands of Howdiemont Bay, which cover easily eroded mudrocks of the Foxton Limestone cycles, although the thin limestones can occasionally be seen. Note that moving northwards along the coast the succession is getting older. After 500 m, outcrops of pale yellow/brown sandstones occur towards the top of the Sugar Sands Limestone cycle. They are notable for well-developed examples of both planar and trough cross-bedding. The exposures are 3-dimensional so that the difference between the two is immediately apparent, especially on bedding planes (parallel straight lines versus curved nested lines). The palaeocurrent direction is towards the southeast and deposition took place in a relatively high-energy mouth bar/distributary channel environment. In the sandstones exposed 20 m farther north (i.e. a few metres lower in the succession), the bedding is contorted into fold structures and locally the sandstone is massive. These features are the result of dewatering and liquefaction of the sand soon after deposition, perhaps induced by seismic shock caused by earthquakes.

Locality 3 (NU 260161). Continue northwestwards across Sugar Sands Bay, also underlain by mudrocks, to the northwest corner. Here the Sugar Sands Limestone is exposed, distinctive for the presence of large gigantoproductid **brachiopods**, up to 15 cm across and mainly in their life position, i.e. concave upwards. The **trace fossil** *Zoophycos* is also present on bedding planes of the limestone, looking like brush marks, 15–30 cm across. Immediately beneath the limestone, and only exposed when the tide is halfway out, is a thin (20 cm) dark grey sandstone, containing brachiopods and many burrows, some going down into the underlying white sandstone. In thin section of this dark sandstone, fish scales and bone fragments are common. The underlying distinctive pale grey to white sandstone, with polygonal structures on the bedding planes and thin dark streaks permeating the rock, is a palaeosol. The cracks are the result of expansion and contraction of the soil and the black streaks are the remains of rootlets. The succession at this locality is the top of one cycle (the palaeosol) and the beginning of the next (the thin dark sandstone and the limestone). After deposition of the white sandstone, perhaps by a river or delta distributary, it was colonized by plants and a soil developed. There was then a **transgression**, and the sea flooded across the coastal plain, reworking the soil to deposit the dark fossiliferous sandstone. Relative sea-level continued to rise and the sea became deeper and clearer enabling the Sugar Sands Limestone to be deposited, in around 20–40 m of water.

Locality 4 (NU 259162). Continue north down the succession through finer grained sediments into mudrocks. Below black shales in the cliff the Iron Scars Limestone is exposed on the foreshore. This limestone has numerous trace fossils on the bedding planes, mostly burrow structures, and there are many **crinoid** ossicles, fragments of **coral, bryozoans** and brachiopods. Below the limestone, a few metres to the north, are black fossiliferous shales and in the cliff, below the shales, a thin coal seam and then a seatearth, crowded with black rootlets, including *Stigmaria* and with nodules of **siderite** present 1 m below the coal. This is another cycle boundary. In this case however, a peat developed on top of a soil (the seatearth) so that a coal seam was eventually produced. The initial deposits of the next cycle were black muds before the limestone was deposited.

Locality 5 (NU 259163). Immediately south of Howick Burn the sediments are part of the Howick Limestone cycle. In the north-facing cliff are two thin coarsening-upward cycles, each 1.5 m thick. Dark mudrock gradually passes up into sandy mudrock, muddy sandstone and then into sandstone. These minor cycles represent the infilling of small bays or lagoons along the coast of a deltaic shoreline. Erosion of the beach sand here may reveal the Howick Limestone, about 5 m from the end of the southern bridge abutment.

Locality 6 (NU 262168). Walk northwards across the foreshore and join a cliff-top path to reach Howick Haven. Here a west-facing cliff shows a classic coarsening-upward succession. On the beach, 3 m from the cliff, the Howick Limestone crops out as a thin (30 cm), dark fossiliferous limestone with bryozoans, **gastropods**, brachiopods and crinoids. At the cliff base, 1 m of dark mudrock with siderite nodules passes up into 1 m of sandy mudrock with isolated ripples and **flaser bedding**, then 3 m of sandstone with cross-lamination and small-scale cross-bedding. The whole package represents a shallowing of the environment, recording the approach of a sandy shoreline.

In the upper part of the cliff, there is a large erosion surface with angular blocks of sandstone above it. This channel and its infill are the product of recent glaciation and have nothing to do with the Carboniferous sediments, deposited some 320–340 **Ma** ago.

Locality 7 (NU 263172). Walk north along the cliff path to Rumbling Kern, a small sandy bay surrounded by cliffs of sandstone, formerly quarried. In this little bay, towards the bottom of the cliff, above a metre of shale, the Howick Limestone is exposed as large discontinuous pillow-shaped nodules, a metre or more across. At the very base of the cliff, a thin (15 cm) coal seam above some 20 cm of pale-grey seatearth again represents the end of one cycle of deposition and the beginning of the next. However, of particular note here is that above the Howick Limestone and 1 m of mudrock with siderite nodules (as at Howick Haven), a prominent coarse sandstone is developed. Its base is sharp and erosive, and there are large rafts of plant and peat (now coal) in the lower part. Around this bay and to the north and south for several hundred metres, the sandstone shows spectacular large scale cross-bedding, mostly directed to the east. This sandstone, reaching 8 m in thickness, was deposited in a major fluvial braided channel transporting sand from the west/northwest to a delta plain/delta front probably located a considerable distance to the east/southeast.

Locality 8 (NU 260179). Walk northwards along the cliff-top path past the Bathing House, seeing Dunstanburgh Castle in the far distance. The low cliffs here are of the channel sandstone with conspicuous cross-bedding. From above Howick Bay there is a fine view towards Cullernose Point, streaked white by the nesting birds. In the near distance about 200 m ahead, the Howick Fault runs east–west across the foreshore. The main feature seen from this viewpoint is the northern end of the major fluvial channel (Figs. 7.2, 7.3). At low tide, look down and seawards across the foreshore exposures to see the basal erosion surface of the channel rise stratigraphically towards the

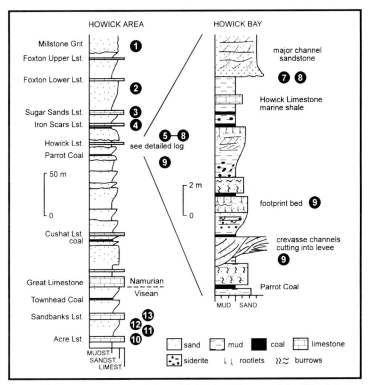

Figure 7.2 Stratigraphy of the mid-Carboniferous of the Howick area, Northumberland, with a detailed log of the Upper Limestone Group sediments in the southern part of Howick Bay.

north. There is a conspicuous bed of sandstone (a seatearth) at the top of the channel infill which can be followed south and then southeastwards out to sea as a result of a small **synclinal** structure. The sandstone within the channel shows bedding surfaces dipping gently towards the south, the result of lateral accretion of the channel margin. Again the channel cuts down to within a metre of the Howick Limestone (which crops out along the far side of a small inlet). A little farther north, the same succession as at Howick Haven can be seen, where the channel sandstone is absent. Overall, this and the last two localities together clearly demonstrate the discrete, localized nature of a major downcutting channel into the marine shales above the Howick

Figure 7.3 The northern end of the major channel within the Howick Limestone cycle. Locality 8, southern part of Howick Bay. *Photo:* M. E. Tucker.

Limestone. It suggests that there was a major change in base-level, which may have been the result of a large fall in relative sea-level.

Locality 9 (NU 259179). Descend to the southeast corner of Howick Bay where the remains of amphibian footprints can be seen on the hummocky surface of a sandstone bed 20 cm below a prominent thin coal seam at the base of the east–west running cliff (Scarboro & Tucker 1995). These footprints, averaging 18 cm in length and 14 cm in width, are now poorly preserved, but it should be possible to discern a trackway of 6 prints, 3 each side, with a central groove where the body was dragged through the sand. In the better preserved footprints, 5 digits could be distinguished and some have a mud rim. The sand became vegetated and penetrated by numerous rootlets and *Stigmaria* which disturbed the footprint surface and account for its hummocky nature. The footprints, probably formed by a temno-spondyl amphibian crawling out onto damp sand from a nearby embayment or lake, were preserved by the deposition of a thin sheet of sand over the surface, probably from the flooding of a small channel. They are some of the oldest footprints in Britain.

Figure 7.4 Two channel sandstones (bases outlined) showing lateral accretion from right to left. The level of the amphibian footprints (arrow) is overlain by a thin coal seam. Locality 9, southwest corner of Howick Bay. Nesting fulmars near cliff top provide scale. *Photo:* M. E. Tucker.

In the north–south running cliff in the corner of the bay, two channel structures show lateral accretion (Fig. 7.4). In the cliff on the right (to the north) a 1.5 m thick mudrock to fine sandstone coarsening upward unit can be seen which, in the central part of the cliff, is cut by a shallow channel filled with sandstone showing inclined bedding to the south. These dipping surfaces are produced by lateral accretion (meandering) of the channel. This small channel is then cut into by a larger channel to the left (Fig. 7.4). This arrangement has been interpreted as levee sediments (the coarsening-upward unit) cut into by a **crevasse** channel, and then the main distributary channel taking the path of the crevasse channel (Elliott, 1976).

Above the channel infill sediments, a thin coal seam represents abandonment of the channels and the growth of peat in a swamp environment. An overlying 2.5 m thick mudrock to sandstone coarsening upward package (the footprint surface is towards the top of this) with another thin coal seam (Figs. 7.2, 7.4) represents a small delta prograding into a shallow bay or lagoon along the delta front. These sediments, towards the top of the Cushat Limestone cycle, are

89

all coastal plain/delta plain deposits and the rapid lateral and vertical changes in facies represent the local variation in these depositional environments.

Locality 10 (NU 259180). Continue northwards on the foreshore to the Howick Fault, a major east–west structure which cuts out some 200 m of strata (Figs. 7.1, 7.2). On the south side of the fault the Howick/ Cushat Limestone cycle sediments (lower part of the Upper Carboniferous) are much affected by small-scale faulting and deformed into a broad **hanging-wall anticline**. On the north side is the Acre Limestone (upper part of the Lower Carboniferous), consisting of fossiliferous limestone beds and calcareous mudrocks. The main Howick Fault dips 40° southwards. Along the fault line **dolerite** of Whin Sill type has been intruded, best seen at mid to low tide in the mid-foreshore area.

Locality 11 (NU 258183). Farther north on the foreshore, crinoids, brachiopods and corals, as well as **calcite**-filled tension gashes, can be seen in the Acre Limestone. The limestone passes up into dark shales, locally with **pyrite** and calcareous nodules. In the cliff, these mudrocks pass up into sandy shales, muddy sandstones and then pale grey sandstones in a clear coarsening-upward package. The sandstones here show excellent examples of **hummocky cross-stratification** (Reynolds, 1992) on the scale 0.5–1 m in wavelength; there are also thin, graded and cross-laminated sandstone beds. Burrows and nodules are also present. These sedimentary structures are typical of storm waves and storm currents, and indicate deposition in the transition zone of a storm-dominated sandy shoreline.

Locality 12 (NU 260186). Northwards on the foreshore, the sandstones with storm structures give way to cross-bedded and planar-bedded white sandstone with a range of burrow structures. One of these, *Eione moniliforme*, has a very distinctive beaded appearance. These sediments were deposited in shallower water, in the shoreface and foreshore environments. At the small cliff running out to sea, the top of this Acre Limestone cycle is well exposed, and the white sandstone is now massive and hard with black streaks. This is almost a ganister: a very clean, quartzitic seatearth. A very narrow recess in the cliff, 20 cm wide, is the position of a thin coal seam. This Acre Limestone cycle is distinctive in that it is not the result of delta progradation, but of beach-shoreface progradation. The top part of the small cliff is the Sandbanks Limestone, marking the beginning of the next cycle.

Also of interest here, just south of the small cliff crossing the foreshore, is a narrow **dyke** of Whin Sill material. This dyke is classic in form: it stands up as a metre-high wall, with a narrow zone of hardened sandstone adjacent to the dolerite.

Locality 13 (NU 260187). Climb over the small cliff on to the extensive bedding surface of the Sandbanks Limestone. This limestone, like the others, contains fossil crinoids, brachiopods and corals, and from a small outcrop of the overlying shale by the path up from the beach, fragments of **trilobites** can be found. The Sandbanks Limestone here shows some fine 'whaleback' folds on the lower foreshore. The fold axes are oriented north–south and the folds are asymmetric, with steeper limbs on their western side. There is a major fault in the northwest corner of the bay here, and it is possible that the folds are related to horizontal movement on this fault, which would then be showing dextral strike-slip movement.

Ahead is Cullernose Point, composed of the dolerite of the Whin Sill. The cliff shows well-developed columnar **jointing**, vertical in the central part of the cliff then dipping at a lower angle towards the seaward end of the cliff. This may be the result of the Whin Sill changing its stratigraphic horizon.

8 · The Carboniferous and Permian rocks between Tynemouth and Seaton Sluice

Brian Turner *University of Durham,*
with a contribution on the Permian by
Denys Smith *GEOPERM & University of Durham*

PURPOSE

To examine the stratigraphy and sedimentology of Westphalian B
Coal Measures and Permian rocks along the southern margin of the
Northumberland Basin.

LOGISTICS

The excursion can be completed in one full day depending on tides.
Cars and minibuses can be parked close to all the localities, but car
parks charge a fee from May to September. There is also easy access
by public transport. The excursion is not recommended for large
parties. Although access to all localities is relatively easy, care must be
taken on the slippery seaweed-covered foreshore rocks. Hard hats and
wellingtons are essential; stay clear of unstable overhanging ledges
when examining cliff faces, especially between Hartley Bay and
Collywell Bay where several cliff falls have occurred recently.

Maps

O.S. 1:50 000 Sheet 88 Tyneside & Durham; B.G.S. 1:50 000 Sheet 15
Tynemouth (solid).

GEOLOGICAL BACKGROUND

The area between Tynemouth and Seaton Sluice (Fig. 8.1) lies at the
southern end of the Northumberland coastal plain. It is an area of low,
relatively flat ground covered by a veneer of glacial **till**, modified by
late glacial and post-glacial **solifluction**. As a result, the underlying

solid rocks of Upper Carboniferous and Permian age are exposed only in quarries, cliff faces, rocky headlands and on wave cut platforms.

This stretch of coast provides one of the best exposed sequences of Westphalian B Coal Measures anywhere in Britain. The succession consists of about 115 m of shale, mudstone, siltstone and sandstone arranged in vertically stacked coarsening-upward sequences capped by a **seatearth** and coal seam, interbedded with a number of prominent channel and distributary mouthbar sandbodies, each one named after their outcrop locality (Fig. 8.2). Typical coarsening-upward coal-bearing **facies** sequences consist of (from bottom to top): (1) black shale containing fish and plant debris plus fresh-water **bivalves**; (2) rhythmically banded dark grey mudstone and siltstone, passing upwards into fine-grained sheet sandstone, containing burrows, ripple **cross-lamination** and some small-scale trough cross-bedding; (3) ironstone-bearing seatearth with small rootlets and scattered *Stigmaria*; and (4) coal. **Trace fossils** and plant fragments are common, but body fossils are generally confined to the fresh-water mussel bands above coal seams. Ironstone bands and nodules occur in the shales and mudstones, some of them showing **cone-in-cone** structure.

The coarsening-upward coal-bearing facies sequences result from the gradual infilling of shallow interdistributary bays and lakes by shoal-water **lacustrine** delta complexes originating from overbank flooding and **crevassing** along numerous distributary channels which drained a southerly sloping, low relief coastal alluvial plain remote from open marine influences. The black fossiliferous shales were deposited on the anoxic bottom of unstratified fresh to brackish water lakes, followed by mudstones, siltstones and fine sandstones as the crevasse-splay delta system prograded into the lakes. As the lakes filled with sediment the surface was colonized by vegetation, giving rise to peat swamps and ultimately, *in situ* coal, following compactional subsidence, transgression (mussel bands) and burial. The presence of **faults** and soft, weak shales and mudstones has caused extensive collapse of cliff faces, and the rapid retreat of the coastline due to marine erosion.

At the end of the Carboniferous Period the newly-deposited strata were uplifted and gently folded and faulted during the **Variscan** earth movements and were subjected to perhaps 40 **Ma** of subaerial erosion as the region gradually drifted northwards out of the equatorial belt into the tropics. At least 400 m of Coal Measures were eroded from southeast Northumberland during this phase and a mature desert peneplain was established before the oldest Permian deposits – the

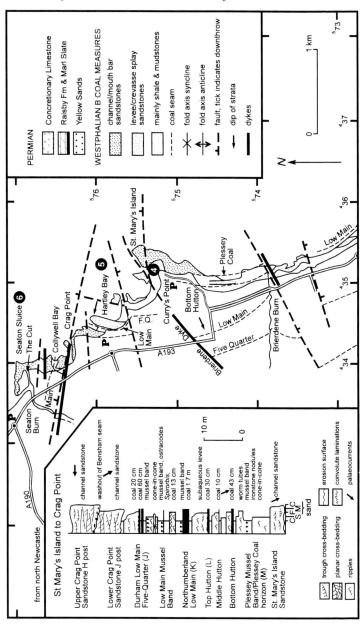

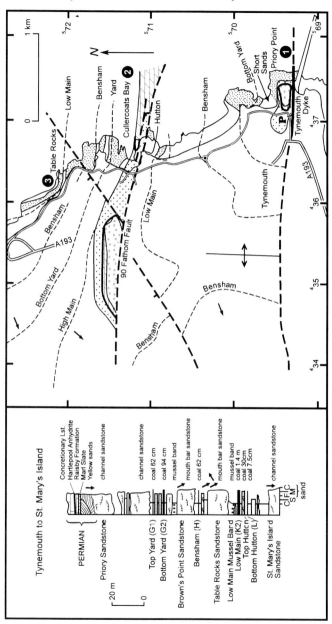

Figure 8.1 Generalized geological map and stratigraphic sections of the coastal area between Tynemouth and Seaton Sluice showing localities mentioned in the text.

260–255 Ma wind-blown Yellow Sands – were preserved in west-southwest–east-northeast ridges or **draa**. The desert was flooded and the ridges inundated some 255 Ma ago when the almost landlocked Zechstein Sea was formed; this sea was subsequently filled with a thick cyclic sequence of marine **carbonate** sediments and **evaporites** during the last 5–7 Ma of the Permian Period. These cyclic rocks form a continuous cover in coastal districts south of the Tyne (Fig. 1) and in the undersea area off the Northumbrian coast, but are preserved on land in southeast Northumberland in only a few isolated **outliers** in each of which the sequence is thin and incomplete. Two of these outliers, at Tynemouth and Cullercoats, are included in this excursion.

EXCURSION DETAILS

Locality 1, Tynemouth Cliff (NZ 374694), not at high tide nor for the infirm; binoculars helpful. Park in ticket car park (NZ 371694) opposite The Gibralter Rock, and take narrow road and paved footpath south and east for c.550 m to the landward end of North Pier; steps here afford access northwards to the boulder-strewn and very uneven rock platform, which can be followed (with care) around the headland and back to the car park via Short Sands and a paved and stepped path up the bay head. The round trip takes up to 2½ hours.

The spectacular coarse dark red mottling of the otherwise buff-coloured Carboniferous (Coal Measures) sandstone that forms the rock platform and lower part of the cliff immediately north of North Pier, was caused by desert weathering in early Permian time. The scattered boulders of Scandinavian **schist** and **gneiss** are thought to have been brought to Tynemouth by ice during the Pleistocene Period. Many of the other boulders are ships' ballast. The 3–4 m wide west–east subvertical **basaltic** Tynemouth **Dyke** cuts the sandstone of the shore platform (Fig. 8.3) and is a member of the 58 Ma (Palaeocene) Mull Swarm. Conspicuously cross-bedded Yellow Sands (c.9 m) **unconformably** overlie the Coal Measures sandstone in the adjoining cliff. Continue northwards c.130 m past the buttresses and pipe, pausing at intervals thereafter to examine a markedly scoured erosion surface that divides the Coal Measures sandstone into two unequal parts (Fig. 8.1, bottom left inset). The upper of these locally contains, at its base, a striking variegated breccia of angular to subrounded fragments of red and purple mudstone, siltstone and ironstone in a mainly buff-coloured sandstone matrix; this **breccia** is thought to be the remains of muddy sediments that were formerly

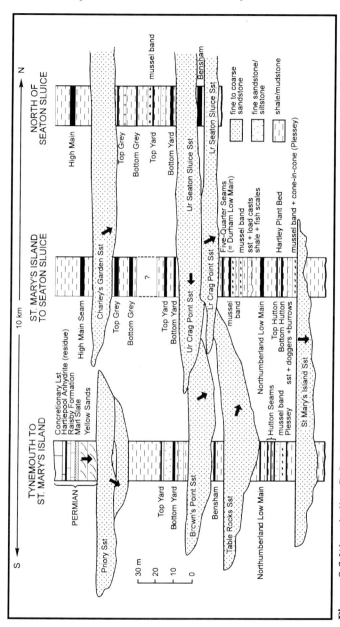

Figure 8.2 Westphalian B Coal Measures stratigraphy between Tynemouth and Seaton Sluice. The arrows indicate the flow direction of currents responsible for the deposition of each major sandbody.

associated with the Metal (= ?Top Grey or Top Five-Quarter) Coal and were ripped up and redeposited by turbulent floodwaters. An exceptionally complex large pouch of mauve and red, fine-grained, laminated sandstone at the cliff foot north of the pipe may be a load cast, caused by liquefaction of the sand (causing 'quick' conditions) soon after it was deposited; a sand volcano may have existed here but was later eroded away.

North of the buttresses the full succession in the cliff is visible, and comprises late Permian Magnesian Limestone in addition to the Yellow Sands and Coal Measures; most of the sequence is inaccessible or dangerously steep and scaling should not be attempted. The upper part of the sequence here is similar to that at the equivalent but more accessible exposure at Trow Point (Excursion 13, Locality 1), 3 km to the south-southeast, but the disturbed (resedimented) beds at the top of the Raisby Formation are here represented partly by a highly unusual debris-flow. This deposit passes southwards in about 30 m from the northeast corner of the headland into a rock composed of tabular to subrounded **clasts** of Raisby Formation **dolostone** in a 30–50% matrix of wind-abraded coarse **quartz** grains and, after a further 30 m, into a **conglomerate**-like vuggy rock composed mainly of Raisby Formation dolostone clasts in a sparse sand matrix; look for large fallen blocks to examine in detail. Clues to the origin of these

Figure 8.3 The Tynemouth Dyke (Locality 1). *Photo:* C. T. Scrutton.

unusual rocks come from Claxheugh Rock and Downhill Quarry, both in western Sunderland, where massive downslope submarine slides at the end of Raisby Formation time created canyons that in both places (and presumably others too) cut down through the Marl Slate into the Yellow Sands. Most of the Permian units may be traced westwards along the north face of the headland as they rise very gently to crop across the Castle forediteh; in spring and summer the niches marking the positions of the Marl Slate and the residue of the Hartlepool **Anhydrite** furnish favoured nesting sites for seabirds, especially kittiwakes.

Locality 2, Cullercoats Bay (NZ 365714). Access is by slipway off the promenade road at each end of the bay. The point at the southern end of Cullercoats Bay lies immediately north of the Ninety Fathom Fault (Fig. 8.1) which is part of a major east–west trending fault system defining the southern margin of the Northumberland Basin; this is an asymmetric, extensional **half-graben** that became filled with over 4 km of sediment during Carboniferous time. The Ninety Fathom Fault is best exposed on the south side of the point where it **downthrows** strata to the north by about 150 m, bringing Upper Carboniferous Coal Measure shales and mudstones associated with the Hutton Coal seam against Permian Yellow Sands. Mineralized fractures and **joints** in the Yellow Sands, close to the fault, bind the rock together, enabling it to resist erosion by the sea; the unmineralized sandstone between the joints has been eroded by the sea to form caves, good examples of which can be seen at the base of the cliff at the back of the bay. The fault plane at the surface **dips** about 35° northwards. On its south side several small folds, with their axes perpendicular to the fault plane, together with the northerly dip of the beds, have created basin and dome structures in the centre of which is the Top Hutton seam and overlying sandstone. North of the fault a faulted **syncline plunges** seawards. Some 30 m of Permian Yellow Sands, of probable late Lower Permian age, are well exposed at the back of the bay where the structural and sedimentological features of the unit can be examined in detail except at high tide.

The Yellow Sands contain mainly medium to coarse, well rounded and well sorted grains, poorly cemented by a patchy **calcite** cement, except near the Ninety Fathom Fault where it was locally firmly cemented by **baryte** derived from fluids moving up along the fault plane in the underlying Coal Measures. The sandstone is rather friable at outcrop and contains small calcite-rich nodules, and **cataclastic veinlets** of granular quartz close to the Ninety Fathom

Fault. At depth the sandstone is grey owing to the presence of **pyrite** which oxidizes near the surface to **limonite**, giving the sands their distinctive yellow colour. The Yellow Sands are interpreted as a formation of sinuous-crested dunes superimposed on about eleven parallel ridges of sand, trending west-southwest to east-northeast. The ridges were deposited on an easterly sloping peneplain of Coal Measure rocks, separated and underlain by thin discontinuous interdune breccias. The preserved parts of the dunes contain large-scale tabular and wedge shaped cross-bedding deposited by bi-directional seasonal winds blowing towards the south and northwest.

The Yellow Sands are sharply overlain by the Marl Slate which is a dark grey, laminated, bituminous **dolomitic** shale or shaley dolomite up to 1.5 m thick. This is well exposed at low tide on the foreshore just inside the south pier where it occurs in the nose of a syncline. The Marl Slate, which at Cullercoats has yielded an extensive fish fauna of early Upper Permian age and rarer land-derived plants, passes seawards beneath the pier under a ledge of pale yellow bedded dolomite that forms the centre of the syncline. The Marl Slate is overlain by the Raisby Formation which consists of a lower part of limestone and an upper part of predominantly dolomitized limestone. Disturbance of strata at the top of the Raisby Formation, seen on the foreshore at Cullercoats, is attributed to the effects of submarine slumping and sliding that took place on an easterly facing basin margin slope at the end of Raisby Formation time.

The Marl Slate was deposited in a stratified, partly anoxic sea up to 200 m deep soon after the initial transgression of the Upper Permian Zechstein Sea. Evidence of thinning and wedging out of the Marl Slate against Lower Permian sand dunes, suggests the development of shallow water conditions and ?interdunal lagoons. The Zechstein Sea quickly submerged the desert landscape concomitant with a change to more open marine conditions, and the Raisby Formation here was deposited under moderate water depths on an easterly facing carbonate ramp.

Locality 3, Table Rocks (NZ 364722). From Cullercoats, park just beyond a sharp left-hand bend after the coast road rejoins the cliff top. The most extensively exposed sandstone in the Westphalian B succession is the Table Rocks Sandstone which is about 16 m thick at this, its type locality (Fig. 8.1). The lower part of the sandstone is exposed at low tide between the foreshore and the sea wall; the upper part is exposed in a cliff, 5–15 m high, that can be traced laterally for some 600 m northwest–southeast below the promenade at the top of the seawall. Stratigraphically the sandstone lies between the Durham

Low Main (= Five-Quarter) and Bensham coal seams, where it forms part of a coarsening-upward **progradational** sequence overlying organic-rich interdistributary bay and peat swamp deposits. The sandstone has a lobate subsurface plan geometry, a medium to coarse grain-size and radial palaeocurrent trend, all of which suggests that it was deposited as a mouthbar sandbody forming the proximal part of a crevasse-splay delta system that prograded eastwards across the local and regional palaeoslope into a fresh to brackish water interdistributary bay lake. Well bedded flaggy sandstone, containing abundant low angle, lenticular cross-beds with tangentially based foresets, represents the main axial part of the delta mouth bar. Massive, erosively-based sandstone with large-scale lenticular cross-bedding, and large **diagenetic** ironstone **concretions** up to 2 m diameter, formed in a subaqueous distributary channel seen at the northern and southern end of the outcrop. A lithologically more variable cross-bedded sandstone, containing sandy mudstone and carbonaceous mudstone, was deposited at the margins of the mouth bar. Mudstone exposed at low tide below the seawall where it is transitional into the overlying flaggy sandstone represents the distal mouth bar fringe. All these **lithological** components of the Table Rocks sandbody are characteristically lenticular in shape (Fig. 8.4) on several scales, producing a series of lens-shaped packages.

Figure 8.4 Lenticular bed geometries in the Table Rocks Sandstone (Locality 3). *Photo:* B.R. Turner.

Locality 4, Curry's Point (NZ 350754) and St Mary's Island (NZ 353755). Turn off the A193 coast road (NZ 346747) and follow the signs to St Mary's Island; park in the large car park just before the concrete causeway to the island. The succession here consists of the St Mary's Island Sandstone overlain by up to five vertically stacked, coarsening-upward coal-bearing facies sequences, each up to 5 m thick. These are exposed in a number of fault blocks between St Mary's Island and Hartley Bay (Fig. 8.1), a distance of just over 500 m. The St Mary's Island Sandstone is a predominantly cross-bedded channel sandbody deposited by currents flowing to the south. It is the lowest bed exposed along this stretch of coastline, although the base of the sandstone is not seen. It is a well jointed sandstone, cut by small faults on the south side; on the north side it is terminated by the Brierdene Fault. Note the sub-Permian reddening of the sandstone, especially down joints. At low tide, small rounded pieces of pale green **apatite**, can be found in the rock pools on the north side of the causeway. The apatite is the remains of the cargo of the 'City of Gothenburg' which was wrecked on the rocks here in 1891, whilst sailing from Montreal to South Shields. In the small bay immediately north of Curry's Point black shales containing large brown ironstone nodules can be seen. The nodules, which weather out from the softer shales, contain a fresh-water mussel band and well developed cone-in-cone structures. To the north the shales are overlain by a thin rippled cross-laminated sandstone, containing prominent, funnel-shaped bivalve escape structures, that forms a conspicuous ledge at the edge of a small wave cut platform. Bedding surfaces on top of the sandstone show prominent intersecting joint sets and large diagenetic ironstone nodules. In the low cliff above the sandstone, a seatearth with plant rootlets and *Stigmaria* is overlain by the Bottom Hutton Coal seam. The higher part of the cliff is a soft till, containing exotic clasts of various lithologies such as Whin **Sill dolerite** and Lower Carboniferous limestone. It was deposited 15–17 000 years ago during the last (Devensian) glaciation to have affected the area prior to the present interglacial period. A break in the cliff immediately to the north marks the position of the Brierdene Fault.

At low tide the next locality, Hartley Bay, can be reached by walking along the foreshore if time permits, but the cliff-top path is quicker and easier.

Locality 5, Hartley Bay (NZ 344758). As an alternative to the cliff-top path between St Mary's Island and Collywell Bay, limited parking is available above Hartley Bay by the caravan club park at Old Hartley.

Steps lead down to the beach at the southern end of the bay. The exposures in Hartley Bay have been relatively unaffected by faulting and include all the strata between the 1.7 m thick Northumberland Low Main Coal seam and the 1 m thick Five-Quarter seam (Fig. 8.2). The Northumberland Low Main seam can be seen below the steps, and by the concrete support wall at the bottom of the steps where it is partly covered by cliff fall material. The seam can be traced at intervals along the base of the cliff where it is underlain by a pyrite-bearing seatearth and fine-grained sandstone. The sandstone contains ripple cross-lamination, with scattered burrows, **bioturbation** and shallow scour features. Rippled bedding surfaces and plant fossils occur in some of the fallen sandstone blocks at the foot of the cliff; the cliff face itself provides excellent exposures of two typical coarsening-upward coal-bearing sequences. These gradually decline to foreshore level approaching Crag Point, at the northern end of Hartley Bay, due to the shallow northeasterly dip. A 13 cm thick coal seam at the cliff base on the promontory immediately north of the steps in Hartley Bay, is overlain by a mussel band containing **ostracodes** and *Spirorbis* (worm tubes). About 1 m below the coal seam is a thin sandstone characterized by convolute laminations, attributed to reactivation of the nearby Ninety Fathom Fault.

Continuing northwards along the foreshore toward Crag Point the wave cut sandstone platform contains some rectangular hollows about 1 m deep, now partially filled by wave reworked pebbles, cobbles and boulders. These hollows are thought to be the bottom of old bell-pits, dug from the cliff top during Napoleonic times to mine the thick Northumberland Low Main Coal seam beneath the sandstone. The cliff top must then have extended much further seaward. At the back of the bay a small sandbody about halfway up the cliff face contains well developed southerly dipping lateral accretion surfaces indicative of point bar deposition within a small meandering channel. Evidence of faulting can be seen in the lower part of the cliff approaching the northernmost end of Hartley Bay which is defined by the prominent, but unstable cliffs at Crag Point (Fig. 8.1). The sharp contrast between sandstone and shale here is due to the Crag Point Fault, which downthrows strata 15 m to the north. The cliffs consist of two channel sandstones: a lower fine-grained sandstone characterized by wedge and trough cross-bedding with ripple cross-lamination and horizontal laminations, and an upper coarse-grained, predominantly planar cross-bedded sandstone (Fig. 8.2) parts of which have collapsed making access around the point difficult. The contact between the sandstones is a well defined erosion surface overlain by a conglomerate containing small quartz pebbles, coal clasts and plant material.

Locality 6, Seaton Sluice (NZ 338769). Turn off the A193 coast road (NZ 337768) by the road bridge across Seaton Burn at Seaton Sluice to the car park in front of The King's Arms. Cross the wooden footbridge over 'the cut', a deep vertical trench cut through sandstone. Turn right down the footpath and proceed on to the old wharf on the north side of the cut, which is 274 × 9 by 16 m deep. The cut was excavated in 1761–64 by Thomas Delaval when Seaton Sluice was a busy industrial area and coal port, to provide a new harbour entrance, especially for coal barges. Two sandstones are exposed along the foreshore and in the cut, but northwards they dip into the subsurface. The lower, which has been correlated with the Lower Crag Point Sandstone, is a fine-grained, **argillaceous** sandstone characterized by lenticular bed geometries and predominantly wedge and trough shaped cross-bedding deposited by currents flowing to the southeast (Fig. 8.2). The upper sandstone, in comparison, is much coarser-grained and more **feldspathic**, with anomalous concentrations of **garnet**. It is characterized by sheet-like bed geometries, and structured internally by planar and less commonly trough cross-bedding arranged in cosets up to 50 cm thick. At the seaward end of the cut on the north side, troughs migrated down the lee faces of some larger scale bars or sandwaves. Aggradation of these bars, possibly as part of large sandflat complexes, can be compared with the development of medial and lateral sand bars forming today in sandy braided river systems. The base of the sandstone is defined by an erosion surface, locally overlain by small pebbles and granules of quartz, **siderite**, coal clasts and plant material, which has removed all of the intervening Bensham Coal seam and associated strata from this part of the succession (Fig. 8.2). The Upper Seaton Sluice Sandstone has been correlated with the Upper Crag Point Sandstone and unlike other channel sandbodies in the succession it was deposited by a braided river system flowing westwards, across rather than down the local and regional southerly palaeoslope. It is thought to have been deposited in response to a sudden lowering of depositional base level due to fault controlled uplift of the Farne **Granite** and older Carboniferous strata located not more than 80 km off the present day Northumberland coast.

9 · The Lower Carboniferous at Bowden Doors, Roddam Dene and the Coquet Gorge

Brian Turner and **Andrew Heard**
University of Durham

PURPOSE

To examine three contrasting styles of Lower Carboniferous sedimentation within the northern part of the Northumberland Basin: braided river sheet sandstones, alluvial fan conglomerates and coastal alluvial plain sediments. The area also contains a great variety of glacial landforms including **drumlins** and glacial **overflow channels**, which are particularly well developed south of Wooler.

LOGISTICS

All three localities can be visited in one full day (Fig. 9.1). Roadside parking is available at Bowden Doors and Coquet Gorge. Bowden Doors involves rough walking across hummocky ground and along footpaths. The site is an **S.S.S.I.** and a popular location for rock climbing. At Coquet Gorge it is necessary to cross the river and care must be taken on the steep, shaley slopes above the river on the south side of the gorge. The area lies within a military firing range and prior permission for a visit should be sought from the Military Authorities at Otterburn Camp (tel: (0191) 261 1046). Access to Roddam Dene is more difficult. The most convenient parking is on farmland for which permission (not necessary in advance) should be sought from the farmer at Roddam Hall. The banks of the dene are very steep, muddy, and slippery when wet. Easier, but less convenient access is provided by a track, large enough for a car, crossing Roddam Burn about 0.75 km above the dene where the conglomerates are replaced by sandstones. The best exposures occur below this locality in the bed and banks of the burn, and it is necessary to keep crossing the stream at intervals. Wellington boots are essential for this section, even at low water. Roddam Dene is not recommended for large parties.

Maps

O.S. 1:50 000 Sheets 75 Berwick-upon-Tweed, 80 Cheviot Hills & Kielder Forest area, and 81 Alnwick & Morpeth; B.G.S. 1:50 000 Sheets 4 Holy Island (solid), 5 The Cheviot, and 6 Alnwick; B.G.S. 1:63 360 Sheets 4 Holy Island (drift), and 8 Elsdon.

GEOLOGICAL BACKGROUND

The geology of northern England consists of a sedimentary cover of Carboniferous and Permo-Triassic rocks resting **unconformably** on Lower Palaeozoic basement. The basement is made up of **folded** and **faulted** sedimentary and volcanic rocks, originally deposited in the proto-Atlantic Iapetus Ocean (Fig. 3a). Subduction of the ocean to the northwest led to its closure by the end of the Silurian along the Iapetus **suture** zone, a major Lower Palaeozoic **tectonic** line which trends in a northeasterly direction beneath the Northumberland Carboniferous cover. Extensional reactivation of a northerly dipping crustal scale shear zone, associated with the Iapetus suture, led to fault controlled subsidence and the initiation of the Northumberland Basin. The basin is a rifted **half-graben** oriented northeast–southwest across northern England with its deepest part adjacent to the Stublick-Ninety Fathom Fault system defining its southern margin. During Carboniferous times the basin was filled with over 4 km of sediment, with predominantly marine conditions in the southwest and continental conditions in the northeast. The oldest sediments in the basin are locally developed alluvial fan **conglomerates**, such as the Roddam Dene Conglomerate, deposited along the flanks of the Cheviot massif, a highly dissected Lower Devonian volcano intruded by **granite**. Cheviot granite and volcanics, as well as the underlying Silurian **greywackes** occur as **clasts** in the conglomerates. The conglomerates are overlain and interbedded with coastal alluvial plain channel sandstones and fluvio-**lacustrine** interchannel siltstones, shales and impure limestone (**cementstones**) of the Cementstone Group. The overlying succession comprises: (1) fault-controlled braided river sediments of the Fell Sandstone Group; (2) coastal and lower delta plain sediments of the Scremerston Coal Group; (3) cyclically-deposited marine **transgressive-regressive** sediments of the Limestone Groups, which were deposited during the change from syn-rift to post-rift phases of basin development; (4) a thin sequence of fluvio-deltaic sediments of Millstone Grit type; and (5) coal-bearing coastal alluvial plain Coal Measure sediments marking the end of Carboniferous sedimentation in the Northumberland Basin.

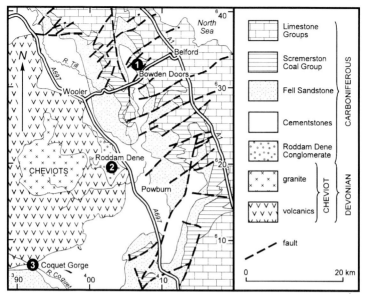

Figure 9.1 Generalized geological map of northeast Northumberland showing excursion localities.

The area provides a striking example of the way in which topography is affected by geological factors. The Fell Sandstone, located on the faulted northeast limb of the Holburn **Anticline**, forms a rugged west-facing scarp overlooking the Wooler valley. The scarp acts as a drainage barrier separating the Cheviot Hills from the sea, and deflecting the drainage of local rivers, such as the Till, to the north. The grass and heather-covered slopes of the Cheviots are dissected by a number of valleys, including Roddam Burn, which forms a steep, wooded gorge (Roddam Dene) cut through Late Devonian-Early Carboniferous sandstones and conglomerates on the eastern side of the Cheviots. On the south side the Coquet River has cut a similar gorge through less resistant Cementstone Group strata west of Alwinton.

EXCURSION DETAILS

Locality 1, Bowden Doors (NU 070327). From the centre of Belford village, just off the A1, take the B6349 Wooler road and turn right into the Hazelrigg-Lowick road. Vehicles can be parked on the grass verge by the second gate on the right, next to the sign saying 'Beware of Bull'. Cross the hummocky grass and heather-covered dip slope on the southwest side of the road to the top of Bowden Doors crag (the word *doors* means place of wild animals) and follow the footpath along the base of the crag to the south.

The Fell Sandstone is one of the most prominent **lithological** units in the Lower Carboniferous succession of the Northumberland Basin. It is also a very important aquifer and the main source of water for Berwick-upon-Tweed. At Bowden Doors the Fell Sandstone forms a 450 m long crag, oriented north-northwest–south-southeast parallel to the local palaeocurrent direction. Stratigraphically the outcrop lies near the top of the Fell Sandstone succession close to the contact with the overlying Scremerston Coal Group, on the faulted northeast limb of the Holburn Anticline, a compressional structure of late Carboniferous age. The crag face, which attains a height of about 8 m at the southern end, consists of two main **facies** (Fig. 9.2). The first comprises moderately sorted, fine to medium-grained sandstone which becomes finer when traced to the south in the downcurrent direction. Where it occurs it always lies beneath the second facies. The sandstone is mainly structureless but contains some undulating diffuse and isolated sets of **cross-strata** in addition to local water escape and flame structures. This facies has a sharp, planar contact with the second facies above, and the contact between them can be traced along most of the crag face. The general characteristics of this predominantly structureless facies suggests that: (1) it was deposited

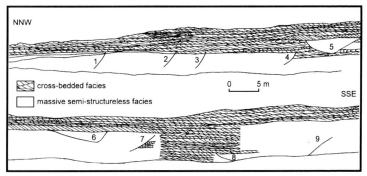

Figure 9.2 Tracing from photograph of Bowden Doors Crag showing lithofacies and location of some of the mass-flow emplaced channels numbered 1–9.

rapidly from a flow overloaded with sediment, thereby promoting homogenisation and liquefaction of the sediment on pore fluid expulsion; or (2) it was liquefied after deposition, perhaps by contemporaneous fault movement.

The second facies is represented by a fine to medium-grained trough and planar cross-bedded sandstone. Deformed **foresets**, attributed to shear by sediment-laden water acting on top of the original sandy bedform, are common and vary from simple puckering of the foresets to completely overturned and recumbently folded foresets. Cross-beds are sometimes organized into complex associations of smaller scale cross-beds superimposed on larger ones, deposited mainly as channel bars and in-channel dunes or mega-ripples. Small steep-sided channel-like features, oriented perpendicular to the main channel trend, cut the face of the crag at various levels and are filled with sand identical to that into which they have been emplaced (Fig. 9.3). Although the margins of the channels are very steep they show no evidence of scour or slumping, and apart from faint marginal laminations they lack grading or well defined sedimentary structures. These features suggest that the channels originated from bank collapse and the development of sediment-laden mass flows moving across the channel along scoured, pre-channelized pathways,

Figure 9.3 Mass-flow emplaced, steep-sided, sand-filled channel in the Fell Sandstone at Bowden Doors. *Photo:* B. R. Turner.

in front of large sandy bedforms. The Fell Sandstone was deposited during a phase of source area uplift and intrabasinal fault activity, by perennial braided river systems **prograding** across the Northumberland Basin towards the south and southwest. Plots of palaeodrainage patterns suggest that the rivers were largely confined to small intrabasinal graben structures connected by a number of transfer zones located between overlapping fault segments.

The top of Bowden Doors crag provides spectacular views of the surrounding countryside. To the west across the Wooler valley one can see the prominent rounded slopes of the resistant Cheviot volcanic dome. Large areas of the Wooler valley, underlain by softer, more easily eroded Cementstones, are covered by ice deposited **till** erosionally moulded into drumlins. Glacial overflow channels are well developed on or near the eastern side of the Cheviots, where the large Powburn (Fig. 9.1) channel has cut through a sandstone crag providing easy passage for the A697 Wooler-Newcastle road. Looking east from Bowden Doors the dip slope of the Fell Sandstone falls away gently towards the sea, interrupted in places by the discontinuous resistant crags of the Whin **Sill dolerite** which is quarried locally at Belford for road metal.

Locality 2, Roddam Dene (NU 025205). Take the Roddam Dene turning off the A697 Wooler Road about 8 km south of Wooler. Follow the road up the hill to Roddam Dene Hall, where permission to visit the site should be sought from the farmer (prior permission is not necessary). Immediately after passing the farm house on the left, turn right through a gate into the fields and continue along a track passing through a second farm gate. After parking walk alongside a wooded area on the right keeping close to the fence and after about 100 m climb the fence and descend carefully down the steep banks into Roddam Burn. Care should be taken in wet weather as the banks are slippy.

The earliest deposits in the Northumberland Basin are the locally developed conglomerates of late-Devonian or early Carboniferous age, which crop out around the flanks of the Cheviot Massif at Roddam Dene (the best exposed), Ramshope Burn and Windy Gyle. The Roddam Dene conglomerate, which has a maximum estimated thickness of 170 m, is cut into three segments by faults. It is a massive conglomerate containing subangular to subrounded pebble to boulder size clasts (4–256 mm in diameter) of Cheviot **andesite**, with minor amounts of Palaeozoic sediments and rare Cheviot **granophyre**, set in a poorly-sorted, mottled red and green clay-rich, sandstone. The conglomerate consists of: (1) a lower, matrix supported, weakly

Figure 9.4 Clast to matrix supported, massive alluvial fan conglomerate, Roddam Dene. *Photo:* B. R. Turner.

stratified and **imbricate** conglomerate with local sandstone lenses; (2) a middle, coarser, more massive conglomerate and; (3) an upper, better sorted, clast supported, coarsening-upward conglomerate associated with trough cross-bedded sandstone and **palaeosols**. The conglomerate is sharply, and erosively overlain by trough cross-bedded, rippled and plane bedded, fining-upward red sandstones and siltstones. The conglomerates were deposited predominantly as gravel bars within a braided river system draining the medial parts of a semi-arid alluvial fan, derived from an uplifted, fault-controlled ridge (?Harthope Fault) to the north. The overlying sandstones were deposited by a different fluvial system, on the distal parts of an alluvial floodplain oriented east–west, and sourced in part from the adjacent flanks of the Cheviot.

Locality 3, Coquet Gorge (NT 905061). From the B6341 Rothbury to Otterburn Road take the turning to Sharperton and Alwinton about 6 km west of Rothbury. Follow the narrow tarred road from Alwinton to Coquet Gorge, about 1.5 km west of Alwinton. Cars can be parked off the road at a number of localities. Easiest access is by way of the footpath at the western end of the gorge which crosses the end of Kay

Crag as it descends into the valley, adjacent to a farm fence. The river must be crossed to examine the cliff section on the south side of the River Coquet, and wellington boots are essential, even at low water. The best exposures occur in the upper part of the cliff and are only accessible via small erosional gullies. Care must be taken on the steep, loose shaley slopes, especially in wet weather. A rough track ascends the eastern end of the cliff but exposures along the track are poor. Prior permission is necessary to visit this site (see Logistics).

At this locality the River Coquet cuts a spectacular gorge through part of the Cementstone Group. The cliffs rise some 50 m above the river at Barrow Scar and provide the best exposures of Cementstones in Northumberland. A fault north of the road brings up Lower Old Red Sandstone lavas (see Excursion 4) against Cementstones, while to the south of the gorge another fault **downthrows** the Fell Sandstone and Scremerston Coal Group. The Cementstone section along the gorge consists of thin sandstones (<1 m) interbedded with thicker (1–2 m), softer shales and subordinate impure limestones or cementstones (<30 cm). A striking feature of the cliff section is the absence of thick, prominent channel sandbodies similar to those seen in the Cementstone Group in the Tweed Basin. Exposures also occur in the bed, and at intervals along the northern bank of the river. Although the sandstones in the succession may contain cross-bedding in the lower part, they are predominantly ripple cross-laminated with bedding surfaces showing a variety of ripple marks, dominated by straight to slightly sinuous types with crest-line bifurcation. The sandstones are highly **micaceous**, burrowed and contain plant material and **trace fossils**. Root-penetrated fine sandstones and siltstones occur beneath dark, carbonaceous-rich shale. The thicker shale sequences contain ironstone **concretions**, plant material and silty interbeds with trace fossils such as *Crossopodia* (formed by arthropods) on bedding under-surfaces. Small calcite-lined cavities, representing **pseudomorphs** of **calcite** after original **evaporite** minerals are present in the cementstones. They also contain fine shaley partings, plant material and **brachiopods**, some of which are locally **pyritized**. Shelly fossils are more common than in the Cementstones at Burnmouth in the Tweed Basin (see Excursion 2), possibly because of the greater marine influence on sedimentation at Coquet Gorge. Occasional thick lenticular sandstones occur within the more regularly interbedded Cementstone succession, a good example of which is the cliff-forming Kay Crag sandstone at the western end of Coquet Gorge on the north side of the river. A local spring line occurs below the base of the crag near the top of the underlying shale-dominated part of the sequence. Kay Crag sandstone is an 8 m thick, coarse to medium grained, highly micaceous (white and black mica), profusely cross-bedded sandstone. The scoured base of the sandstone is overlain by **intraclasts** of shale, siltstone and plant material locally concentrated into a basal channel **lag** conglomerate. The sandstone was deposited by a low sinuosity distributary channel flowing to the southwest, across a dry, low relief coastal alluvial plain subjected to periodic marine incursions from the south. The origins of the cementstones are discussed in more detail in Excursion 2.

Figure 9.5 Gorge cut by the River Coquet in the Cementstone Group (Lower Carboniferous) below Barrow Scar (Locality 3). *Photo*: C. T. Scrutton.

10 · The geology of the North Tyne and Saughtree

Michael Money *Mason Pittendrigh, Consulting Engineers*, **Bert Randall** *formerly University of Newcastle upon Tyne* and **Brian Turner** *University of Durham*

PURPOSE

To study the Old Red Sandstone and Lower Carboniferous rocks of the North Tyne valley and the Saughtree area, the sedimentology of the Scremerston Coal Group and the intrusive phenomena of the Whin **Sill**. Observations are made on the geomorphology and on some geological aspects of the construction of the Kielder Dam.

LOGISTICS

The excursion is not suitable for large parties. Permission must be obtained in advance from Tarmac Roadstone (Eastern) Ltd (Tel: (01434) 681443) for access to Barrasford Quarry (Localities 1–6). Protective helmets must be worn and an indemnity form signed. Park either on the left at the quarry entrance (NY 909740) or, for Locality 6 only, in Gunnerton (NY 905750).

Lewis Burn (Locality 9) is on Forestry Commission land and prior permission for visits should be sought from the local Forestry Commission Offices in Bellingham (Tel: (01434) 220242). Wellington boots are essential.

Localities 11–14 are in unfenced sheep country (avoid lambing and keep dogs under control) with mainly single-track roads. Park clear of passing places.

Maps

O.S. 1:50 000 Sheets 80 Cheviot Hills & Kielder Forest, 87 Hexham & Haltwhistle; B.G.S. 1:63 360 Sheets 7 Kielder Castle, 8 Elsdon, 11 (Scotland) Langholm; B.G.S. 1:50 000 Sheets 13 Bellingham, 17E (Scotland) Jedburgh.

GEOLOGICAL BACKGROUND

The sedimentary rocks seen on this excursion occur on the north-western margin of the Northumberland Trough, on a basement of Silurian **greywackes**. These are generally poorly exposed, have few distinctive mappable **lithologies** and contain only very rare diagnostic fossils. The Silurian is overlain with strong **unconformity** by predominantly fluviatile sediments of the Upper Old Red Sandstone. The actual surface of unconformity is rarely exposed in this area but is the equivalent of Hutton's Unconformity seen in Excursion 1. The O.R.S. is succeeded, apparently **conformably**, by basic Birrenswark Lavas. Traditionally these have been taken to be the basal member of the Carboniferous and they form a convenient and mappable horizon. In detail, however, they interdigitate with and are succeeded by sandstones of O.R.S. lithology. Local Lower Carboniferous stratigraphy is confused by the lack of a recent overview. The Dinantian sub-divisions adopted in most recent B.G.S. accounts of the Border area are from the base up: Lower, Middle and Upper Border Groups, Lower and Upper Liddesdale Groups. In very broad terms, the Lower and Middle Border Groups correspond to the Cementstone and Fell Sandstone Groups, and the Upper Border Group corresponds to the Scremerston Coal Group.

The Whin Sill intrusion was emplaced at the end of the Carboniferous. It is the type sill having been named by the old lead miners in Co. Durham before its recognition as an igneous rock. The Whin Sill around Barrasford is notable for its unusual intrusive relations. The sill **transgresses** northeast-southwest from above to below the Oxford Limestone over some 2 km of outcrop. In the region of transgression the full thickness of the limestone can be found both above and below the sill and large rafts of shale and limestone occur within it. In addition the **dip** slope, which here is overlain by the limestone, is diversified by minor west facing scarps formed by offshoots from the upper surface of the sill. The maximum thickness of sill in the quarry is 40 m but there are rapid regional thickness variations. The main rock of the sill is **dolerite** of renowned uniformity, but with many local textural and compositional variations.

Much of the route of the excursion runs parallel to the line of the Border Counties Railway (BCR) opened fully to traffic by the North British Railway in 1862, and closed to passengers in 1956. A major reason for promoting the line was the exploitation of the Plashetts Coal seam (Locality 9), but other collieries, works and quarries opened along the route, of which Barrasford is the only working survivor.

EXCURSION DETAILS

Barrasford Quarry

The quarry (Fig. 10.1) is rapidly expanding and consequently the features seen vary from time to time.

Locality 1 (NY 916745). From the quarry entrance, take the roadway south of the crushing and grading machinery to the southeast wall on the second quarry road that traverses the quarry wall. Here the upper contact of the sill with the Oxford Limestone is exposed although some of it may soon be obscured by quarry tipping. The sill is chilled visibly for c.2 m. The overlying limestone, although **metamorphosed**, still contains identifiable **brachiopods, corals** and **crinoids**.

Locality 2 (NY 917747). Returning to the quarry floor walk about 300 m northeast. The south wall now shows one of the southeast dipping offshoots from the sill's upper surface which cuts across the overlying limestone. Here the quarry, at this level, narrows and to the northwest the exposure in the dolerite cliff shows low-angle fractures along which are shale inclusions.

Locality 3 (NY 919750) is at the northeast end of the Quarry. The overlying limestone has been stripped off the upper surface of the sill. A metre or so below its chilled margin is a thick zone with numerous **amygdales**, wholly or partially filled with **quartz** (so crystal terminations can often be seen), **calcite** and some iron sulphides. In fallen blocks, the amygdales are 50–150 mm in diameter, have a flat base parallel to the sill's upper contact and a domed top. Underlying these amygdales is a 10–15 mm layer of rock which is coarser and more acid in composition than the normal dolerite.

Locality 4 (NY 917747). Here numerous large blocks of whinstone show different varieties of the sill. These include thin sheets (10–200 mm) of dolerite-**pegmatite**, quartz-calcite amygdales underlain by pegmatite, **tachylite** veins intruded into dolerite, grey or pink **aplite** veins (up to 10 mm thick), and **mineral veins**. The latter, typically 20 mm thick, are common along the major near-vertical **joints** of the sill. There are two types; the first being composed of white calcite with white, purple-cored quartz, which typically has prism faces developed. The second type carries **galena**, **sphalerite**, **baryte** and brassy-yellow sulphides plus quartz and calcite, and is probably related to the Alston Block mineralisation.

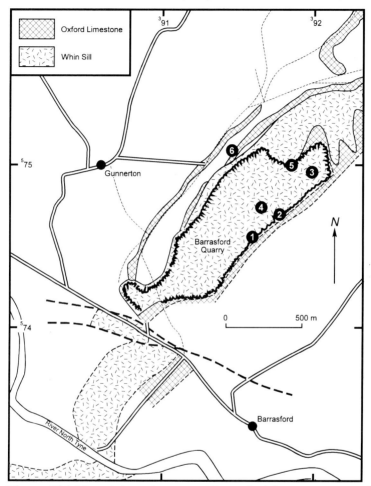

Figure 10.1 Map of the region around Barrasford Quarry.

Locality 5 (NY 917750). Here, looking south, is a good view of the offshoot from the top of the sill cutting through the limestone previously seen at Locality 2. To the northeast the limestone has been stripped off the sill. Just beyond the eastern quarry boundary is a westward facing scarp, due to a low angle offshoot from the top of the sill rising through the superincumbent limestone.

Locality 6 (NY 915751). From a new gate in the quarry boundary (NY 918710), cross a field to another gate into the field containing a disused quarry in the Oxford Limestone, here below the Whin Sill. The full thickness of the limestone is visible; some of the fossils are coated by the **alga** *Osagia*. At the top of the quarry face weathered and shaly-looking limestone contains fossils preserved as external moulds. Near the western end of the quarry is a small doleritic intrusion and a low angle fracture dipping southeast. Above the limestone its dip slope is a grass covered shelf terminated to the southeast by rising ground where spotted shale is revealed by rabbit burrowing. Above this is a scarp of Whin Sill only 2–3 m high.

About 120 m west in the old quarry face (Fig. 10.2), the limestone is upturned and then enclosed within the sill as large flat lying rafts. To the west the limestone can be seen below the sill. As the Oxford Limestone was above the sill in the main quarry (localities 1, 2 & 5) it appears that the sill was probably intruded along a low angle fracture.

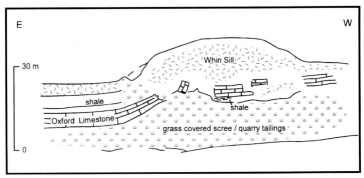

Figure 10.2 Diagrammatic sketch of Gunnerton Crag (Locality 6).

Return to the quarry car-park by walking southwest along the path to the north of the escarpment (along the line of an old railway that used to carry dolerite to Barrasford from another quarry 1.5 km to the northeast). If parked at Gunnerton take the farm track running to the west.

North Tyne – Saughtree

On leaving Barrasford Quarry turn right to Wark Bridge (5 ton weight limit), cross the River North Tyne, and follow the B6320 towards Bellingham. Cross the river again on Bellingham Bridge and turn left, following signs to Kielder. The dam is not conspicuous when approached on this road and the reservoir comes into view suddenly. Turn right on to the road across the dam, signposted Hawkhope Car Park (toilets).

Locality 7, Kielder Dam (NY 708882). Kielder Reservoir is one of the largest man-made bodies of water in Europe. Water stored in the lake is not taken directly into supply but is used to regulate the flow of the North Tyne, and can be extracted further downstream at Riding Mill and transferred via aqueducts, largely in tunnels, to the Rivers Wear and Tees. Walk to the end of the dam or up to the memorial stone to view the downstream face and the original valley profile. The dam is an embankment constructed largely of glacial **till** excavated from the valley floor below top water level. It was sited on a long mound of till extending most of the way across the valley in order to minimize the quantity of fill required. Water is discharged from the power station into a stilling basin at the toe of the dam which also receives flow from the spillway, the large concrete channel and weir at the end of the dam. The draw-off tower in the water enables water to be abstracted from different levels in the reservoir and fed through pipes in a tunnel under the dam either to the turbines in the power station or directly to the river via the stilling basin. All of these concrete structures requiring sound foundations are sited at this end of the dam because the river had cut down close to rock on this side of the valley. The base of the pre-glacial valley is lower and more central in the present valley. The upstream slope of the dam, at normal water levels, is faced with concrete blocks to provide wave protection. Riprap, or rock revetment, was used at lower levels and this was mostly quarried from within the reservoir (see Locality 8), although some was also imported from Barrasford.

Return to the main road, turn right, pass the Tower Knowe Visitor Centre and after 7 km, turn right into the Mounces Viewpoint (toilets).

Locality 8, Mounces Viewpoint (NY 657887). Walk up to the South Viewpoint for a good view of the lake. Although the valley has been glaciated it does not have the classic U-shaped cross-section; it is not straight and there are major tributary valleys on both sides. The slopes are generally smooth and the **drift** cover, especially where exposed by erosion on the lake margins, shows that much material is of local origin and probably deposited by **solifluction**. On the opposite lake shore is a quarry in a **dyke**, compositionally similar to and

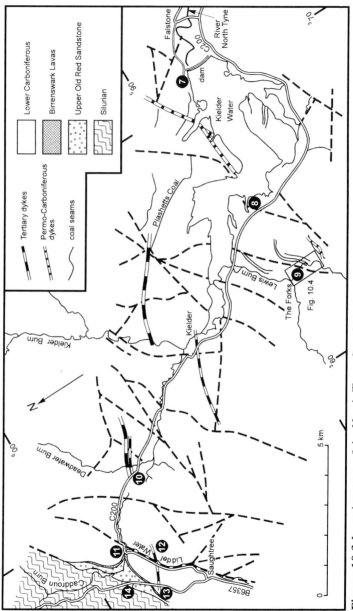

Figure 10.3 Location map of the North Tyne–Saughtree area.

probably intruded contemporaneously with the Whin Sill and forming part of the High Green or Highfield complex of roughly east-west en-**echelon** dykes. The quarry was opened and worked to supply aggregates and revetment stone for construction of the dam, to minimize the traffic of construction materials into the area. Compare the difficulty of quarrying a narrow vertical dyke with the ease of working a long and accessible face in the Whin Sill (localities 1–6).

Return to the road and turn right. After 2 km, take the signposted forest track to Lewis Burn (cars and minibuses only) to the Forks at the confluence of Lewis Burn and Akenshaw Burn. Turn left just before the bridge and park off the track by a steep sandstone cliff. There are no good places to turn round below the Old Stone Bridge over Lewis Burn about 1.5 km above the Forks. Alternative parking is available just across the Old Stone Bridge (Fig. 10.4).

Locality 9, Lewis Burn (NY 631888). The section here is most completely and continuously exposed when the water level in the burn is low. Good exposures are also present at intervals in the hillside alongside the forestry track.

Structurally the area consists of a series of **anticlines** and **synclines** superimposed on a major, extensively **faulted** synclinal structure. Lewis Burn provides one of the best exposures of Lower Carboniferous Scremerston Coal Group strata (Lewis Burn Beds) in Northeast England, especially above its confluence with the Aken-shaw Burn where up to 250 m of the middle part of the succession is continuously exposed on the southeast side of the southeasterly downthrowing Megg's Linn Fault (Fig. 10.4). The beds dip c.20° southeast, except along the fault plane where they dip 60° southeast. Lithologically the succession is dominated by shales and sandstones with subordinate limestones, **seatearths** and coals. The limestones are generally thin, **argillaceous**, fossiliferous **biomicrites**. The shales, containing ironstone ribs and nodules, are also fossiliferous with plants, **bryozoans**, **bivalves**, **gastropods** and brachiopods. Bivalves such as pectens, myolinides and *Sanguinolites* are particularly abundant but become subordinate to brachiopods in the more sandy upper part of the succession where limestones are less common and coal seams thicker. A particularly fossiliferous shale occurs below the first marine *in situ* limestone in the succession, exposed in the southeast bank of the burn below the Old Stone Bridge (Fig. 10.4). Some of the shale sequences along Lewis Burn attain thicknesses of at least 30 m, some of the thickest shales recorded from the Lower Carboniferous anywhere in Northumberland. Shales and associated coals in the

Scremerston Coal Group have attracted considerable interest because of their potential as hydrocarbon source rocks. The coals in the Lewis Burn section have been worked in the past, especially the Lewis Burn Kiln Coal (70 cm thick) and the Lewis Burn House Coal (45 cm thick) (Fig. 10.3). The Plashetts seam is the thickest coal, no longer exposed but reported to be at least 1.5 m thick.

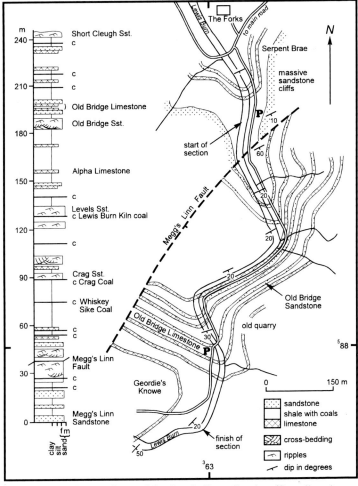

Figure 10.4 The geology of the Lewis Burn Section (Locality 9).

The sandstones in the succession are locally thick (15–45 m) and predominantly lenticular in character. They are fine to medium-grained and contain trough **cross-bedding**, flat bedding, ripple cross-lamination and siltstone and mudstone partings. Most sandstones contain carbonaceous plant material and are burrowed and **bioturbated**; a few are fossiliferous. The succession is characterized by three types of **facies** sequence. The first type is a fluvially-dominated fining-upward sequence composed of an erosively-based, coarse to fine sandstone passing up into mainly non-marine siltstone and shale with rare **cementstone** type limestone capped by seatearth and coal. The second facies sequence coarsens upwards from fossiliferous shelf and prodelta shales or limestones into fine to medium-grained, trough cross-bedded, delta front sheet sands capped by seatearth and coal. Coarsening-upward **progradational** facies sequences are less common in this part of the succession but increase in abundance upwards. The third facies sequence is more marine in character and consists of limestone, shale and sandstone, lacking any fining or coarsening-upward trends, which grade upwards into seatearth and coal. Within these marine packages shell-rich beds, containing crinoids indicative of fully marine conditions, are interbedded with poorly fossiliferous beds and the sandstones are profusely cross-bedded, burrowed and bioturbated. All these sequences owe their origin to interaction between fluvial and marine processes along a low relief, humid lower delta plain characterized by repeated phases of fluvially-induced delta progradation, abandonment and marine transgression. Rapid delta shifting and transgression effectively prevented the development of thick coals. A feature of these sequences is the lateral persistence and argillaceous nature of the marine sediments, and their thickness, which suggests that the sea may have been deeper at this time than during deposition of the lower part of the succession.

Return to the road and turn left towards Kielder Village. 1 km beyond the village, the North Tyne, here reduced to a shallow stream due to headwater capture by the Liddel Water across the Border, is crossed on a stone bridge. After a further 2.4 km stop on the nearside verge opposite a pair of houses.

Locality 10, Deadwater (NY 604969). Below to the west is a large area of peat moss that forms the watershed of the Tyne and the Liddel Water. Quarries on the hillside beyond worked Middle Border Group freestone (sandstone) and limestone.

Continue on the road, crossing the border and passing a large double-arch lime kiln on the left. Limestone was worked in shallow quarries on the hillside beyond, but the beds are thin and the overburden increases rapidly into the hillside. After 2.5 km the road emerges from the forest, crosses a stone bridge and a cattle grid. Turn right immediately into a level grassy area by the stream.

Locality 11, Caddroun Burn (NY 584985). The burn flows southeast before it turns sharply to join Liddel Water, and was probably once a tributary of the North Tyne. A small exposure of sandstone dipping downstream, largely under water, at the downstream end of the large circular culvert represents the oldest exposed Carboniferous sediments in the Lower Border Group. Climb over the railway embankment. On its upstream side are exposures of the earliest Carboniferous Birrenswark Lavas below the sandstone. These are **olivine basalts**, often vesicular especially towards the tops of flows, and usually highly weathered. Continue 250 m upstream of the culvert to a small cliff on the west bank showing 5–6 m of Upper Old Red Sandstone. This exposure is loose and overhanging. Traces of drilling suggest it was quarried, probably for railway construction. The O.R.S. here consists mainly of red and mottled sandstones with subordinate mudstones and sandy shales. There are two horizons of **calcrete**, one at the base approximately 10 cm thick and another near the top of the succession about 1.1 m thick. The base of the lavas is visible at the top of the exposure and can be inspected safely in a smaller exposure 20 m upstream where it is vesicular and exhibits spheroidal weathering. The lavas appear to be conformable with the O.R.S. and dip downstream at about 5°. If time permits, further good exposures of the O.R.S. can be seen 400 m upstream in the Caddroun Pots, a series of scour holes in the stream bed.

Rejoin the road. Continue southwest to the second of two prominent rock scars on the left, parking at a lay-by just before a stone wall meets the road at right-angles.

Locality 12, Hudshouse (NY 576978). The scar is steep and unstable and it should be examined from the near bank of the stream. It exhibits two different aspects. On the left are thinly bedded dark shales, mudstones, siltstones and limestones probably of the Middle Border Group. On the right the rock is mostly unstratified and blocky, with rounded corners where weathering has penetrated. This is a dolerite dyke trending approximately northwest–southeast, almost parallel to the face and probably of Tertiary age. The field relations here may appear confusing, but the dyke is not truly vertical and steps back as it rises, while part of it has been undercut by the river and has fallen away to reveal the sediments behind.

Return to the road and note on the northwest side a succession of roughly semicircular landslip scars, probably formed at a time when the river was higher and was actively cutting into the lower slope. Apart from soil creep shown by terracettes these old slips are now reasonably stable. However, within the next 400 m along the road, notice that cuts have been made to widen the road and numerous small scarps show that movements have been reactivated. The slopes above are relatively gentle and are underlain by drift which has probably been soliflucted.

Continue to Saughtree and turn right at the T-junction (NY 561967) on to the B6357. Cross a small stone bridge and notice further examples of landslipping on the drift slopes to the left. Cross a cattle grid and park in a lay-by, immediately after a stone bridge which crosses the stream to the left.

Locality 13, Dawston Burn (NY 568981). This is the site of a BCR viaduct, demolished when the line was closed. Looking downstream from the bridge, outcrops dipping downstream at low angles are of Lower Border Group sandstones, possibly the equivalent of the Whita Sandstone of the Langholm area. These beds underlie the drift in the slopes to the right, but above the line of the old railway, scattered stream exposures are mainly in the O.R.S. The hills that form the northwest skyline (Saughtree Fell) are underlain by Silurian greywackes. The oldest rocks thus occupy the highest ground. The field relations in this area are obscure due to the lack of exposure but some outcrops of the O.R.S. have vertical bedding, suggesting faulting or **monoclinal folding**, or both.

The same succession is discontinuously exposed in the Dawston Burn for 1 km upstream of the bridge, but is difficult to see if the water is high. Unless the transport can follow, it may be best to examine the lower part of the section, return to the lay-by and then drive to Locality 14.

As in the Caddroun Burn, the beds dip downstream and older strata are encountered upstream. The Lower Border Group is represented mainly by sandstone, although there are a few exposures of shales. A dyke which may be the extension of the Hudshouse Dyke cuts the section. The Birrenswark Lavas crop out approximately 400 m upstream of the bridge and may be traced up the slope southeast of the road. Sandstones of the Upper O.R.S. underlie the lavas but differ little in lithology from some of the Carboniferous sandstones.

From the lay-by continue 1 km up the road to the end of the safety fence. Here the stream swings away from the road and it is possible to park on a grassy track to the left.

Locality 14 (NY 574989). On the slope across the stream there is a rather vegetated exposure of the O.R.S. which dips downstream at about 20° and consists of planar and cross-bedded red sandstones with some pebbly horizons, particularly towards the base. To the right of this, and in the stream bed, Silurian greywackes crop out, dipping downstream at 55–60°. These are greywacke-siltstones and mudstones of Wenlock age with poorly developed **cleavage**. The unconformity between the O.R.S. and the Silurian is not exposed.

If continuing up the valley, as the road climbs, further exposures of weathered greywackes will be seen along the roadside. 200 m beyond the cattle grid stop on the left at the entrance to a disused quarry. In clear weather, the Tyne-Liddel watershed can be seen beyond the deep valley of the Caddroun Burn.

11 · Carboniferous rocks of the Roman Wall and Haltwhistle Burn

Mick Jones *University of Newcastle upon Tyne*

PURPOSE

The area is outstanding by virtue of three interrelated features: the outcrop of the Whin **Sill**, the associated geomorphology, and the siting of Hadrian's Wall on its outcrop. The excursion will cover all three elements together with the stratigraphy of the local succession which spans the Dinantian/Namurian boundary.

LOGISTICS

The excursion is in three parts: the dip and scarp topography along the B6318 (Military Road) from Sewing Shields to Cawfields (Fig. 11.1, Localities 1, 2; less than 1 hr). The geology and archaeology of Cawfields Quarry area (Locality 3; 1 hr). An easy 3 km walk along an old railway track from Cawfields, down Haltwhistle Burn to Haltwhistle and the A69 (Fig. 11.3, Localities 4–7; 2 hrs). For groups, the return walk from Locality 7 could be avoided if a car could be parked at either end. Parking, refreshments and toilet facilities are widely available in the area.

Maps

O.S. 1:50 000/1:25 000 Hadrian's Wall; 1:50 000 Sheets 86 Haltwhistle, Bewcastle & Alston, 87 Hexham & Haltwhistle; B.G.S. 1:50 000 Sheets 13 Bellingham, 18 Brampton (both solid and drift editions), 19 Hexham.

GEOLOGICAL BACKGROUND

The striking landforms of the area arise from a combination of three factors. Firstly, the succession exposed, which ranges from the Jew (=

Oxford) Limestone (Dinantian) to the Oakwood Limestone (Namurian) and consists of sediments deposited in typical **Yoredale** cycles. This repeated sequence of limestone, shale, sandstone, shale, coal produces an alternation of hard and soft beds with very different weathering characteristics. Into this succession was intruded the Whin Sill, of variable thickness and frequently **transgressing** from one horizon to another, but very durable and resistant to weathering in comparison to the enclosing sediments. Secondly, the post-Carboniferous uplift of the Cheviot **pluton** resulted in doming of the sediments laid down in the Northumberland Trough, imparting a significant southerly **dip** to the strata in the southwest of the county. Dips of around 15°, coupled with the alternation of hard and soft beds, produced a strong dip and scarp topography. Thirdly, although these conditions occur over most of Northumberland, the spectacular scenery displayed in the Roman Wall area is not evident elsewhere. This is because ice movement in south Northumberland was from west to east, parallel to the **strike** of the beds, as demonstrated by an **erratic** of Cumbrian Shap **Granite** found in the area by Johnson (1952). The movement of ice along the strike direction will have preserved, and possibly enhanced the dip-scarp topography, whereas movement of ice across the strike fills in the shale depressions with glacial debris, flattening out the topography. Drilling in east Northumberland has also revealed strong dip and scarp topography in rockhead underlying the flat ground surface, with thickness of glacial **till** from 0–80 m.

The Roman Wall is an outstanding structure, literally and metaphorically, accentuated in the excursion area by its location on the scarp edge of the Whin Sill outcrop. It is 118 km long, 4.6–6.1 m high and 2.1–3.1 m thick, with accompanying forts and turrets, crossing from one side of the country to the other. Archaeological investigations have revealed that the Wall is a complex frontier zone with a great wealth of Roman remains. In AD 121 Hadrian set out on a tour to examine the military dispositions in his empire and during his visit to Britain he initiated the construction of the wall which had been proposed by his predecessor Trajan to define the limits of the Roman Empire and to defend the Stanegate frontier road. The building of the Wall seems to have been completed by AD 140, and it continued to operate as a fortification and customs control until the final withdrawal of the Romans from Britain in AD 400.

Where the wall was stone built, as far west as Gilsland, the dressed faces were constructed almost exclusively of Carboniferous sandstones, quarried locally. The core was filled with any available rock

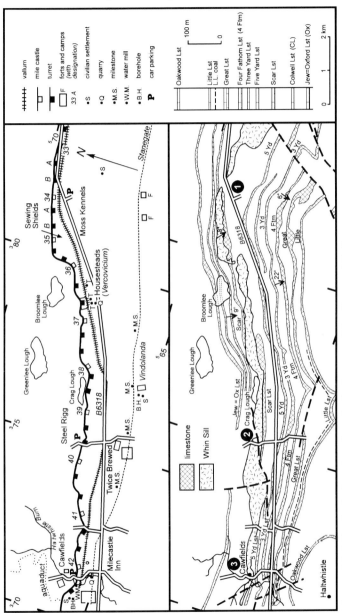

Figure 11.1 Geological and archaeological maps of the Roman Wall country.

material. The Romans found the Whin Sill too hard to work and where the wall crosses the dolerite outcrop on Limestone Bank (NY 875715), the excavation of the vallum is incomplete.

Over the centuries the wall has been gradually degraded, mainly because the dressed stone was an easy source of building material for local farms, houses and castles. The greatest degradation took place following the 1745 Jacobite rebellion when General Wade constructed an east–west road, still known in the north as the Military Road (B6318), to speed troop travel across the country. The first 48 km west from Newcastle were built almost wholly on top of the foundations of the Wall, and only the Wall's construction on the rugged scarp edge of the Whin Sill in the area west of Carrawburgh saved it from total destruction.

EXCURSION DETAILS

Sewing Shields – Cawfields

From Newcastle, take the A69 to Heddon on the Wall. Turn onto the B6318 (Military Road), which from Heddon to Chollerford is almost wholly along the foundations of the Roman Wall. The ditch on the north side and the vallum with the two accompanying mounds on the south can often be clearly seen. Continue westwards, until beyond the fort of Carrawburgh (*Brocolitia*) (NY 859712), the dip and scarp topography of the 'Roman Wall Area' is seen ahead. At Turret T33B (NY 821706) the road leaves the line of the wall which climbs up to the scarp edge of the Whin Sill at Sewing Shields.

Locality 1. From the telephone exchange on the south side of the road (NY 816702), the view west consists of the Whin escarpment, overlain on the lower part of the slope by the Scar Limestone, a peat filled depression, then the conspicuous scarp of the sandstone between the Scar and Five Yard Limestones which the road traverses (Fig. 11.1). Westwards, the scarp and outcrop of the Five Yard Limestone runs parallel to the south side of the road as far as Moss Kennels (NY 803691) just west of which the features break down which suggests **faulting**. Although no fracture has been located, the Whin to the north shows a large break in outcrop and transgression at this point. Housesteads (*Vercovicium*) (NY 793784) can be seen 1 km west on the dip slope of the Whin. The car park is built on the scarp of the sandstone between the Five and Three Yard Limestones and the road continues at this level. To the north the scenery is dominated by the top surface of the Whin, dipping at about 12°, and to the south by the strong scarp feature of the sandstone between the Three Yard and Four Fathom Limestones. Only the upper half of the scarp feature is composed of sandstone, a marked change in vegetation indicating the junction with the underlying shale. The top of the Three Yard Limestone can be seen at the west end of the escarpment (NY 783676). The Whin Sill escarpment is heavily indented, particularly at the site of Milecastle 39 (NY 760767) which has recently been excavated and consolidated. The indentations are probably due to small faults crossing the sill which tend to shatter and weaken the brittle **dolerite**. The most westerly of the indentations is larger and better defined (NY 753675) and can clearly be seen to have acted as a water channel at the end of the last glaciation, draining a lake which lay on the north side of the escarpment, a remnant of which persists as Crag Lough.

Locality 2. Make a short detour at Twice Brewed (NY 751668), turning north to Steel Rigg. From the car park just north of the wall (NY 751677), walk 100 m from the southeast corner along the wall to the edge of the **overflow channel** and a superb view of the Whin escarpment, with its columnar **jointing**, and Crag Lough in the middle distance (Fig. 11.2).

Figure 11.2 The Whin Sill crag at Steel Rigg, with the Roman Wall at its crest and Crag Lough at its foot in the distance (Locality 2). *Photo:* C. T. Scrutton.

Return to the Military Road, which over the next 2 km west has the dip slop of the Whin continuing on the north side but to the south the features are buried under till. They gradually emerge near the junction at NY 730663 where quarries in the Four Fathom Limestone can be seen alongside the road and in the Great Limestone near the skyline; these features strengthen and the Four Fathom Limestone crosses the road at NY 720662. To the south quarries and lime kilns indicate the position of the Great Limestone with further quarries in the sandstone above it.

Turn north at the Milecastle Inn (NY 716660) to Cawfields. Immediately on the right is a good section of the Four Fathom Limestone exposed in an old quarry, while on a raised hillock on the left, between the road and Haltwhistle Burn, is the site of the fortlet that guarded this section of the Stanegate. Between the Four Fathom Limestone and the top surface of the Whin are the remains of old workings in coal below the Three Yard Limestone and **siderite** ironstone bands in shales in the same part of the succession. The most striking feature, however, is the vallum and mounds running along the base of the Whin feature. Continue to Cawfields quarry car park.

Locality 3, Cawfields Quarry (NY 713666). The car park and lake are on the site of the old whinstone quarry which removed not only the scarp of the Sill but also the Roman Wall that ran along its top; working ceased when they approached Milecastle 42 and the break in the continuity of the escarpment.

The top surface of the Sill defines the land surface; a thin skin of **metamorphosed** sediment can be found in places. Columnar jointing is developed perpendicular to the top, cooling surface, of the intrusion. In the old quarry walls on the south side of the car park the fine grained chilled margin of the sill can be seen, but is very thin. More obvious is the band of vesicles 2 m below the top. These formed by gas, released from the magma by reduced pressure as it rose towards the surface. Their presence at a definite level in the sill suggests that the magma close to the surface contact had cooled to a viscosity that prevented the bubbles rising any further, most of the vesicles have later been filled with **calcite**.

Along the north side of the lake, a stile over the low stone wall permits access to the main quarry face, which at its northern end exposes the base of the sill, resting on sandstone dipping southwest at 45°. To the east, behind the quarry face, the Whin escarpment is offset along the line of a small northwest–southeast valley. The valley may mark the position of a fault, **downthrowing** east, displacing the Whin escarpment to the north. Recent geophysical work, however, suggests that the displacement is due to a transgression of the sill and it seems probable that both faulting and transgression are involved. On the east side of the small valley Milecastle 42 occupies a sloping site and has short stubs of broad wall on either side joining on to the narrower linking wall section.

If time permits, the walk westwards from Cawfields via the fort of *Aesica* to Walltown, largely on the Whin dip slope, is very rewarding archaeologically.

Haltwhistle Burn

As well as a good dip section through the Carboniferous succession, Haltwhistle Burn provides an insight into the rich industrial heritage of the area (Fig. 11.3). The Whin quarry at Cawfields was linked by a narrow gauge railway, down the burn to Haltwhistle and the main Newcastle-Carlisle railway. Other industrial activities in the vicinity were mining of ironstone from below the Three Yard Limestone, probably smelted at Haltwhistle; mining of coal from three separate seams; quarrying of the Great and Four Fathom Limestones, burnt in lime kilns for agricultural lime and mortar; quarrying of sandstone for building; mining of **fireclay** for bricks, pots and pipes; quarrying of **ganister** for firebricks for furnace linings; and the working of **galena** for lead and silver.

Locality 4. Approach the burn from the white gate just west of the cottage on the south side of the Military Road (NY 714659). The Four Fathom Limestone is exposed in the stream bed under the road bridge but can only be reached from the south side of the burn. The track down Haltwhistle Burn, mostly the old railway line, is well marked. From the gate, the field surface is the top of the sandstone between the Four Fathom and Great Limestones and it can be seen outcropping in places through the thin soil. At the stream the upper half of the Great Limestone is exposed, about 7 m thick, in well defined **posts** with clay partings; the bedding is disturbed by a small fault crossing just upstream. Further exposures are present in the stream bed but nowhere is the full thickness of the limestone exposed. Overlying the limestone are the Tumbler Beds, calcareous shale with thin bands of limestone, so called because they often show small scale **folding**. On the east side of the burn the shale fragments provide a rich fauna of small **brachiopods, crinoid** ossicles and calyx plates, **echinoid** plates, **corals** and **bryozoa**.

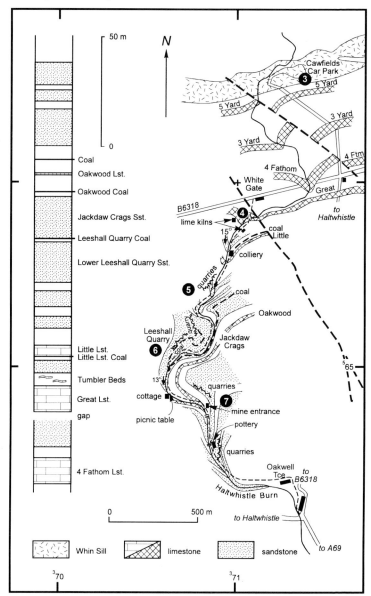

Figure 11.3 Geological map of Haltwhistle Burn.

Downstream, beyond lime kilns on both banks, the basal section of the sandstone above the Great Limestone is exposed in the east bank. It is thin bedded and shows fine detail of sedimentary structures picked out by severe wind erosion in its exposed position. Around the next bend are the remains of the colliery which worked the Little Limestone Coal; the chimney and engine block are still standing. Fragments of the coal can be found and the overlying Little Limestone, rich in bryozoa, is exposed in the hillside behind the chimney; there is a smaller exposure downstream in the west bank. The Little Limestone is rarely exposed, since it is only 3–4 m thick.

Locality 5 (NY 709655). Cross to the west bank by the footbridge. South dipping interbedded massive sandstones and shales are exposed in the banks, with two of numerous quarries in the sandstones adjacent to the footbridge. Apparent changes in the dip of the sandstones downstream, particularly well seen at Jackdaw Crags where the massive sandstone in the east bank, underlain by a thin coal, appears to be synclinal, are due to the frequent changes in stream direction. The dip is constant. Stream erosion across the shale/sandstone alternations has produced a very sinuous course.

Locality 6 (NY 707651). In Leeshall Quarry, on the west bank, two sandstones are separated by a 25 cm coal, the same as that at the base of Jackdaw Crags, underlain by **seatearth** 2 m thick. The sequence reflects the build up of the Carboniferous delta top to water level allowing the growth of plants and the formation of peat. Downstream of Leeshall Quarry the path returns to the east bank via the old railway bridge in which the narrow gauge tracks are still embedded. Continue downstream to the picnic place where an excellent dipping top bedding surface of the Upper Leeshall Quarry Sandstone can be seen in the stream. Stay close to the edge of the stream where the Oakwood Limestone crops out just above water level on the west bank. The exposure continues for 20 m downstream to just above the wooden footbridge. The 2–3 m thick limestone is impure with a high clay content and is a significant marker horizon in this part of the succession dominated by sandstone and shale

Locality 7 (NY 708649). Downstream on the east bank, sandstone, underlain by the shale above the Oakwood Limestone, forms the main face of a large quarry, set back from and running parallel to the burn. Nearby are the remains of another colliery, a drift into the base of the cliff marked by some stone packing and a concrete tunnel from which issues a flow of water, white with alum. The colliery initially worked a thin coal above the Oakwood Limestone but later it mainly mined fireclay for the pottery, recently closed, a few metres ahead. The remains of the kilns and the large sandstone wheels used to grind up the clay are still in the yard and glazed pipes can be found.

On the east side of the burn there is another large sandstone quarry just past the pottery, now used as a coal merchant's yard. Follow the path along the bank and then along the back of a row of old miners' cottages (with its water supply coming out of the bank side in the middle of the row), past the allotments and out on the main road at the east end of Haltwhistle village.

12 · The Quaternary of South Tynedale

Angus Lunn *University of Newcastle upon Tyne*

PURPOSE

To study glacial erosional and depositional features, and post-glacial river terraces, in parts of the Tyne Corridor and North Pennines (Alston Block). Landforms and deposits associated with the final melting of the last ice sheet are conspicuous.

LOGISTICS

A half-day car or coach excursion. All locations are either accessible to the public, or visible from roads or public footpaths. The Whitfield Fell Channel is on private grouse moor, but it can be observed from the road. The recent river terraces at Garrigill can be seen from the Pennine Way but are much better appreciated at ground level; although there is no formal access to the floodplain on the right bank of the South Tyne, that area is much frequented by local children.

Maps

O.S. 1:50 000 Sheet 87 Hexham & Haltwhistle; B.G.S. 1:50 000 sheets 19 Hexham (solid), 25 Alston (solid and drift); Soil Survey of Great Britain 1:63 360 Sheet 19 Hexham.

GEOLOGICAL BACKGROUND

No recent published **drift** or landform mapping has been carried out in the excursion area, other than drift recorded in the course of official soil mapping. Unpublished work by P. J. Vincent, however, concerns the drift, **meltwater channels** and glacial history of part of the area.

All known Quaternary deposits in the area are considered to belong to the Dimlington **Stadial** of the Devensian cold stage (i.e. to the latest ice sheet glaciation of the region, which took place between about 26 000 and 13 000 years ago), or to subsequent periglacial and temperate periods. However, glacially eroded landforms have been shaped over successive glaciations.

Approximate flow lines at the maximum phase of Dimlington Stadial glaciation (continuous arrows) and at a later phase of glaciation (broken arrows) are shown in Fig. 12.2. Later still, during deglaciation, divides became exposed and wasting ice was confined to the valleys. Flow lines are inferred from the limits and direction of carry of **erratics**, the orientation of meltwater channels, **till** characteristics, and the orientation of striae and **drumlins**. At the maximum, much of the area was glaciated by ice orginating to the west, in the Lake District, Vale of Eden and southwest Scotland. However, western ice even at this stage failed to overcome the Cross Fell ice cap and override the highest parts of the main Pennine **fault**-scarp, so that the upper parts of the dales of the Alston Block were occupied only by local Pennine ice. The influence of local Cross Fell ice increased further as incursive Edenside ice thinned after the maximum.

Hartside Pass (NY 6441) is near to the southern limit of erratics carried across the Pennine western escarpment from the Vale of Eden. Further east, erratics from the Lake District etc. have been found in the till of West Allendale as far up-valley as Whitfield (NY 7756), and in East Allendale as far up-valley as Sipton (NY 8550) (Fig. 12.2).

EXCURSION DETAILS

Take the A69 westwards from Hexham. The River Tyne at Hexham, and the South Tyne along the first section of the route, are flanked by alluvial terraces (they are particularly wide at Hexham), which are considered to be Flandrian (present interglacial) in age. Tyne valley villages, such as Haydon Bridge, are sited on one or more of the terraces (Fig. 12.1).

From Hexham to Haydon Bridge, on both sides of the river, the floor of the South Tyne valley above the terraces consists of moundy (**kamiform**), **glaciofluvial** sand and gravel deposits. They occur in a more or less continuous belt, about 2 km wide, with individual mounds rising to some 100 m above the river. The glaciofluvial deposits are banked against till-covered solid rock on either side of the valley. They were deposited in an ice-contact environment at a time when westward retreating ice was transmitting through its stagnant margins enormous volumes of meltwater from the west. The lower

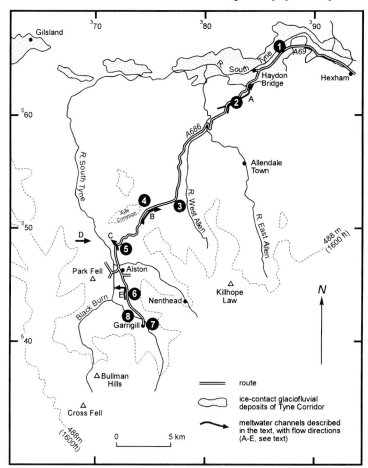

Figure 12.1 Excursion route and glacial features of South
Tynedale, and East and West Allendales.

South Tyne valley was then receiving not only local meltwater but, via
the Tyne Gap at Gilsland, sub- and englacial drainage from the
decaying ice sheet in the Eden valley, the northern Lake District and
southwest Scotland. The belt of moundy sands and gravels continues
westwards through the Tyne Gap into Cumbria.

Individual mounds may be of supra-, en- or sub-glacial origin. Soils
developed on the sands and gravels are brown soils, with ground-

water **gleys** in the depressions, in contrast to the surface-water gleys on tills which are typical of the excursion area generally. The trenching of the South Tyne into the kamiform glaciofluvial deposits may have been accomplished in part by meltwater drainage overflowing the col at Gilsland, from a lake dammed against the western ice sheet after its retreat westwards of the col. The A69 enters this kamiform belt immediately west of the Tyne crossing at Hexham, and a very short detour along the minor road to West Boat (where turning is possible) passes a **kettle hole** on the western side of the road at NY 909656.

Locality 1 (NY 869659) is a segment of old road alongside the present main road on its north side (400 m west of the sign for Woodshield farm), where vehicles may pull up and from which varied sand and gravel mounds may be viewed all around.

Take the A686 Alston road. As far as Langley Castle the road remains among glaciofluvial mounds. It then enters the winding wooded valley of the Langley Burn (A, Fig. 12.1). This is one of a number of northeasterly oriented minor valleys on the southern side of the South Tyne valley. They may have been initiated by meltwater drainage along successive temporary margins of the retreating ice sheet (with lobes convex down the South Tyne valley); the present-day burn is misfit.

Locality 2 (NY 827613). The case for the Langley Burn valley having been initiated as a meltwater channel is strengthened by the virtual absence of a stream in it where it opens out at Langley, and may be further appreciated by turning left for a few metres along the B6295. There, at Locality 2, the valley is seen to continue westwards as a completely dry feature.

Continue along the A686 which becomes coincident with the floor of the channel on passing through Langley Moss. The head of the channel is west of the road, south of Harsondale Law (NY 810612), but the road follows what may be a southern branch almost to the Carts Bog Inn (NY 818606). The west–east orientation of the main western part of the channel, parallel to that of many others in the area, supports a subglacial origin for this section, eroded in a direction accordant with ice sheet flow and surface gradient, even though its eastern extension may have functioned as an ice-marginal channel, as suggested above.

The road descends via hairpin bends (surveyed and laid out by John McAdam himself) to the floor of the Allen valley. The deeply incised meanders of the lower River Allen reflect the difference in elevation between valley floors on the Alston Block and the floor of the South Tyne in the Tyne Corridor. This difference probably resulted from a combination of relative uplift of the Alston Block along the Stublick Fault system, and selective glacial deepening of the Tyne Corridor by high velocity ice streams within successive ice sheets.

Locality 3 (NY 772528). The road climbs out of West Allendale. Pull up 100 m or so after a lane forks left to Ouston and Ninebanks. Looking south-southeastwards up the dale, an asymmetrical cross profile is apparent, typical of all of the North Pennine dales which are aligned transverse to ice movement. Valley sides facing into the direction from which the ice was flowing – in this case the eastern side – have been selectively steepened by glacial erosion, while the opposite, lee sides are gentler. The lee sides were also the main locus of till deposition, and the asymmetric distribution of till in valleys is well seen on B.G.S. Sheet 25 Alston. Additionally, the up-glacier facing, steepened slopes of the Pennine dales exhibit well-developed structural benching, reflecting variations in resistance to erosion of the **Yoredale** strata, and this is probably also a consequence of active glacial erosion on these exposed valley slopes.

The road continues towards the summit of Whitfield Moor. Just before rounding the corner at NY 748520 there is, to the left, an excellent cross-sectional view of the spectacular glacial meltwater channel described at Locality 4.

Locality 4 (NY 742512). Cars can be parked in the lay-by. Entrenched into the summit plateau, 100 m southeast of and parallel to the road, is the Whitfield Fell Channel (Fig. 12.1,B). This is a northeasterly oriented dry valley, now some 20 m deep, eroded in rock (flaggy sandstone and shale), with a multiple head on the divide. It is partly infilled with peat, to a maximum depth of 5 m, and although the visible valley fades away southwestwards near the Northumberland/ Cumbria county boundary, intensive peat coring indicates that the sub-peat valley cuts right through the divide. The channel is interpreted as having formed subglacially by northeasterly directed meltwater streams. The trend of this and of other subglacial meltwater channels in the immediate area, implying an ice surface gradient and therefore ice flow towards the northeast, reflects the strong influence of the ice cap centred on Cross Fell during at least the later part of the Dimlington Stadial. In clear weather Cross Fell, and Great and Little Dun Fells (Great Dun Fell with its conspicuous telecommunications

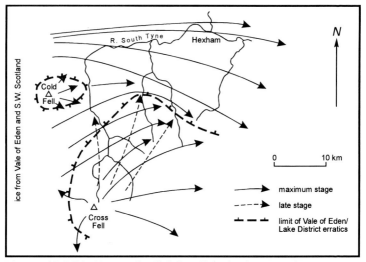

Figure 12.2 Dimlington Stadial flow lines in the excursion area.

sphere) are visible 16 km to the southwest. The plateau surface adjacent to the channel carries blanket peat (up to 4 m deep). A good impression of the double or triple head of the channel is obtained from a point 100 m northeast of the county boundary (walk or drive).

Continue along the A686. Descending towards Alston and South Tynedale the road crosses several short meltwater channels (anomalous, dry valleys) oriented broadly down-slope; these are probably subglacial **chutes**, eroded when the ice had become much thinner than was the case when the Whitfield Fell Channel was formed, and when regional glaciological control of the direction of meltwater drainage was relaxed.

Locality 5 (NY 718484). At this point, where the road crosses a chute (C), there is a small parking place on the corner. The chute can be inspected, and this is a good general viewpoint. Across the Ayle Burn, on Ayle Common (NY 7150), can be seen one of the finest examples in the North Pennines of areal ice scour. The southwestern face of Ayle Common took the full force of Lake District/Vale of Eden ice flowing northeastwards or east-northeastwards over the Pennine escarpment in the Hartside Pass area, and the Yoredale sequence of the Middle and Upper Limestone Groups on the fell is beautifully revealed in the sculpturing of the slopes into benches (both under the improved

The Quaternary of South Tynedale

pastures and meadows below, and the moorland above). The rock-fronted bench, not far above the highest horizontal wall, is developed on the Firestone Sill sandstone. The steep western side of Ayle Common contributes to the glacially-imposed asymmetry of upper South Tynedale; contrast the smooth, tapered spurs visible beyond Ayle Common on the western side of the dale. Looking westwards across South Tynedale, another spectacular meltwater channel (Fig. 12.1,D) can be seen on the western side of the valley, cut into rock and separating the hills Great (NY 685487) and Little Heaplaw. The channel carried subglacial drainage towards the east, and severs the end of a spur.

Take the B6277 Barnard Castle road out of Alston. After 1.5 km the road swings right over Nattrass Gill (note how the place-names change from Anglian to Cumbrian Viking on crossing the county boundary), after which is a straight stretch where it is safe to stop.

Locality 6 (NY 728444). Parallel to the road and about 100 m to the west is a conspicuous shallow marginal or sub-marginal meltwater channel (Fig. 12.1,E), parallel to the contours. It can be examined by walking a short distance down the lane leading to High Nest, which crosses it. It was eroded for about 1 km along the margin of a decaying lobe of ice which lay in the floor of the South Tyne valley, and emptied into Nattrass Gill, which formerly acted as a subglacial chute carrying the meltwaters down towards the valley floor. Across the South Tyne valley to the southwest is a view up the lower valley of the tributary Black Burn, somewhat asymmetrical as a consequence of a northerly component of ice flow from Cross Fell. Directly opposite Locality 6 is Park Fell (NY 699455), the well-developed stoss-and-lee form of which is the obverse of an asymmetrical valley. The up-glacier end (to the southwest) – the stoss slope – is steepened and benched, while the lee end is smoothed, tapered and streamlined. The morphology of Park Fell, like that of Ayle Common, is evidence of the erosive power of the ice which, during maximum phases of glaciation, invaded South Tynedale from the Vale of Eden.

Leave the B6277 3 km from Alston and take the minor road down to Garrigill. Descending towards the village the river terrace upon which the village stands can be clearly picked out in the distance by the parallel field boundary walls which descend from the bluff behind the terrace and then cross it.

Locality 7. Park in Garrigill village, or alongside the road leading southwards from it. At NY 746413, at the southern end of the village,

143

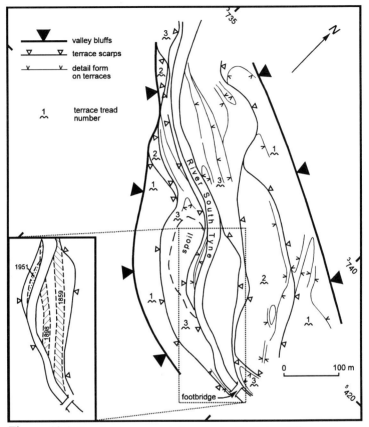

Figure 12.3 Garrigill terraces (after Aspinall, *et al.* 1986).

the terrace can be seen to be rock-defended (the South Tyne has eroded a gorge through the terrace and the underlying Tyne Bottom Limestone) and to consist of cobble gravels. Its surface is at about 7 m above river level, and on the north bank of the present bend in the river is a lower terrace fragment, representing a tight meander eroded into the main terrace at some stage of down-cutting. The main terrace may be part of an outwash train, but there is no evidence of age.

Locality 8 (NY 740418). Walk northwestwards through the village along the minor road on the western side of the South Tyne. At the point where the Pennine Way leaves the road to follow the river towards Alston is a footbridge over the South Tyne. From the bridge can be seen a series of low alluvial terraces. They have been studied in detail by Aspinall *et al.* (1986). The lowest and youngest of the terraces (terrace 3 on Fig. 12.3) is considered by them to be a direct consequence of excess floodplain and channel bed **aggradation** during the main lead-mining period, followed by later incision. Sediment, predominantly fines, was derived from the erosion of river-bank waste dumps, etc. These and other metalliferous river terraces, together with the modern floodplain, are the main habitat of a suite of heavy-metal tolerant plant species ('metallophytes') – which other-wise occur on mine dumps – and include *Minuartia verna* (spring sandwort) and *Thlaspi caerulescens* (alpine penny-cress), both of which are abundant on the floodplain here. Fig 12.3 shows the terraces, and also migration of the river channel over the floodplain during the last 130 years, the information being derived from successive Ordance Survey maps. The three terraces above the present floodplain are clearly visible on the ground, with the higher terraces exhibiting palaeobars and channels. Very low concentrations of heavy metals occur in the higher terraces (terraces 1 and 2), which are between 3 and 6 m above the river. However concentrations are much higher on the lowest right bank terrace (terrace 3), 2 m above the river, and on the floodplain itself. The latter (from the first O.S. map) existed by 1859. The highest concentrations of lead, copper, zinc and cadmium were in fact found in the 1859 river bed, when lead production was at its peak. Clearly the lowest terrace and the present floodplain date from the lead-mining period (eighteenth and nineteenth centuries) and subsequently, while terraces 1 and 2 predate this mining activity but are otherwise of unknown (presumed Flandrian) age. All of these low terraces (1, 2 and 3) post-date the higher one on which Garrigill village is situated.

Garrigill is a starting point for climbing Cross Fell, and should anyone be tempted it is worth noting that the Pennine Way route to the summit passes near to the Bullman Hills (NY 7037) and the Lambgreen Hills (NY 711364). These hills are giant glacial erratics: slabs of the Great Limestone which have been rafted up to 1 km from original outcrop. The larger giant erratics are capped by till and this by blanket peat. (*To climb Cross Fell it is necessary to be properly equipped for fell-walking.*)

Return to Hexham either by the same route, or via Nenthead and Allendale (noting asymmetry in all of the dales).

13 · The Magnesian Limestone between South Shields and Seaham

Denys Smith *GEOPERM* and
University of Durham

PURPOSE

To examine the Permian rocks in the coastal area of County Durham (including Tyne & Wear) and to interpret their mode of origin.

LOGISTICS

This excursion occupies one full day (or two half days) and takes a minimum of 8 hours, including a 1-hour lunch break. All the exposures are close to roads and parking is available nearby. About 25 km travelling, some urban, is involved between the first and last stops. Parts of the coastal sections are not accessible at high tides.

Maps

O.S. 1:50 000 Sheet 88 Tyneside & Durham; B.G.S. 1:50 000 Sheet 21 Sunderland.

GEOLOGICAL BACKGROUND

The highly varied rocks to be seen on this excursion were all formed during the last few million years of the Permian Period and comprise the Yellow Sands Formation and the internationally known and spectacular Magnesian Limestone. The sequence is shown in Fig. 13.1.

Most of the Permian Period in northwest Europe, including County Durham, was dominated by erosion, uplift and reddening of Carboniferous and earlier rocks that had been **faulted** and gently **folded** by the late Carboniferous **Variscan** earth movements. During this time, perhaps for 40 **Ma**, the region drifted slowly northwards from the wet equatorial belt to the dry trade wind belt, where it formed part of one of the great deserts of world history. A mature desert land surface – a peneplain, now represented by the **unconformity** – and the patchy aeolian Yellow Sands (?360–355 Ma old), are all that remains of this prolonged episode.

Subsidence of a broad belt extending from the ancestral Pennines eastwards to Lithuania and Poland created a vast inland drainage basin during the desert phase. A dramatic change of scene late in the Permian period took place when the Boreal Ocean, perhaps following a **glacioeustatic** sea-level rise, broke in from the north, flooding the inland desert basin and instantly (in geological terms – perhaps 5 to 15 years) forming the tropical Zechstein Sea. The middle of this sea was probably initially 200–300 m deep, but was almost completely filled with salts by the end of the period.

The thick and variably fossiliferous Magnesian Limestone of the Durham coastal cliffs was formed on the gentle shallow submarine slopes near the western margin of the Zechstein Sea during the last 5 to 7 Ma of the Permian. The sequence in the cliffs and adjoining inland areas is divided into five major **carbonate** formations that are grouped into three main cyclic units (Fig. 13.1) separated by the insoluble residues of former salts (**halite** and **anhydrite**). The fracturing and foundering of the carbonate rocks resulting from the dissolution of

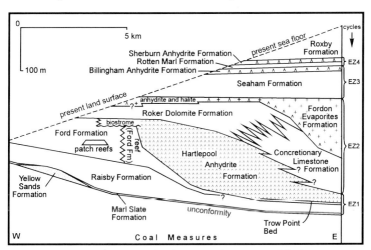

Figure 13.1 Permian strata in the excursion area, with the evaporites restored to their original position. Slightly modified from Smith (1994).

these former salts is one of the three most spectacular features of the Durham coastal cliffs, the others being the striking evidence of downslope submarine slumping and sliding in two of the formations and the bewildering array of **calcite concretions** in the Concretionary Limestone Formation.

The geographical distribution of the main formations of the Magnesian Limestone in northern coastal Durham is shown in Fig. 13.2, together with the approximate position of the recommended stops. The stratigraphical position of the rocks at the localities to be visited is shown on Fig. 13.3. Each of the main formations is seen in at least one location, except the back-reef facies of the Ford Formation, and the Marl Slate which are omitted for logistical reasons. They may be studied at Ford Quarry (NZ 36305720) and Claxheugh Rock (NZ 36305760) respectively (1½ hours required, hard hats).

EXCURSION DETAILS

Locality 1 (NZ 384667), Trow Point (**S.S.S.I.**, no hammering), South Shields (1 hour). Park in Trow Lea car park (NZ 383667), near The Water's Edge. This complex exposure is summarized in Fig. 13.4.

Locality 2 (NZ 385641), Cleadon Park Quarry, northeast corner (30 mins). Park in Quarry Lane, near the junction with Larch Avenue; the face is adjacent. Keep within 100 m of the road. This 3–5 m vertical face is in about the middle of the Concretionary Limestone Formation. Most of the rock is finely laminated unfossiliferous spherulitic limestone but a few thin graded beds are present and these contain moulds of the **bivalves** *Liebea* and *Schizodus*. The spherulites were formed by the recrystallization of the rock whilst it was deeply buried, and are up to about 8 cm across. Some have been slightly rotated and fractured by dissolution. Small patches of buff powdery **dolomite** lie between many of the spherulites and, in the southeast corner of the face, all the limestone locally passes laterally into soft buff **dolostone**. These rocks were probably formed on the low–middle part of the basin-margin slope, in anoxic conditions under perhaps 120–200 m of stratified sea water. The laminites were built up of ?annual couplets of **pelagic** lime mud (winter) and **phytoplankton** (summer); the graded beds are probably **turbidites**, composed of lime mud and lime silt that was originally deposited in oxygenated shallower water on the shelf or higher on the slope and redistributed into the basin by turbid suspension currents.

148

Locality 3 (NZ 398651), northwest end of Marsden Bay, an S.S.S.I. (50 mins, hard hats essential). Park at the northwest end of Marsden Lea car park (NZ 397651) then take the steps to the beach, turning right at the bottom and walk southeast (no farther than the tall narrow stack). The cliffs here are formed mainly of 16–20 m of cream and buff fine-grained dolostone of the Concretionary Limestone Formation. Concentrate for the first 135 m on the general appearance of the rock face

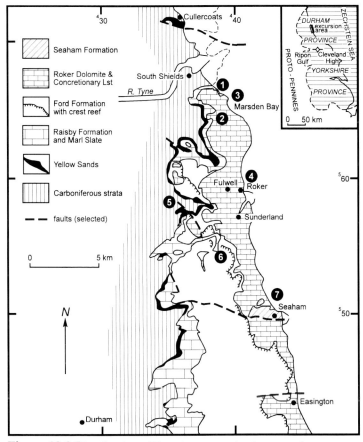

Figure 13.2 Distribution of Permian strata in the excursion area, showing the approximate positions of localities 1–7. Slightly modified from Smith (in Johnson, in press).

from a distance, for this is one of the best places in Britain for seeing the effects of foundering caused by the dissolution of underlying **evaporites**. All the strata have foundered by about the same amount (?60–100m) but some parts have been let down gently and without much dislocation whereas others have had a more complex history of subsidence and are intensely fractured ('**breccia**-gashes'). After the first 135 m inspect the rock in detail. As at Locality 2, it comprises a mixture of finely laminated and unlaminated rock, here mainly fine-grained buff dolostone but also includes unlaminated **oolite**; some of the unlaminated beds, including the oolite, contain moulds of *Liebea*, *Permophorus* and *Schizodus*, many are graded and some have tight folds and shear-planes caused by downslope slumping and sliding. The inferred depositional environment is as for Locality 2.

Locality 4 (NZ 407596), Roker promenade, Sunderland (40 mins). Park in any of several east–west residential roads off the coast road and (from NZ 40685961) proceed down the steps to the beach, noting the large blocks of Concretionary Limestone beside the steps, probably from Fulwell quarries 2 km to the west. Turn right at the bottom, to inspect the c.8 m cliff of Roker Dolomite dolostone. This is unevenly bedded and **dips** gently southwards; it is cream and buff, mainly finely oolitic, soft and porous, and most of the **ooliths** have hollow centres. Tabular **cross-lamination** is present and thin beds of

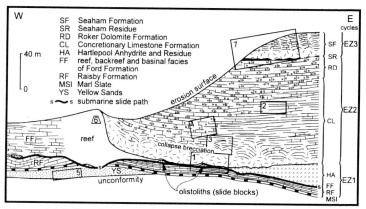

Figure 13.3 Permian strata in the excursion area, showing the approximate stratigraphical positions of localities 1–7. The Hartlepool Anhydrite would not normally be present close to the coast but is included for completeness.

mud- or silt-grade dolostone drape broad low-amplitude ripples. Several disturbed beds up to 0.6 m thick, probably debris-flows, lie on scoured surfaces. Moulds of *Liebea* and *Schizodus* occur in some beds. These rocks were probably formed high on the basin-margin slope, in well-oxygenated water of moderate energy.

The famous 'Cannon-Ball Rocks' are the second main feature of interest at Roker. They form a rounded mass against the promenade just north of the steps and comprise a tightly-packed assemblage of

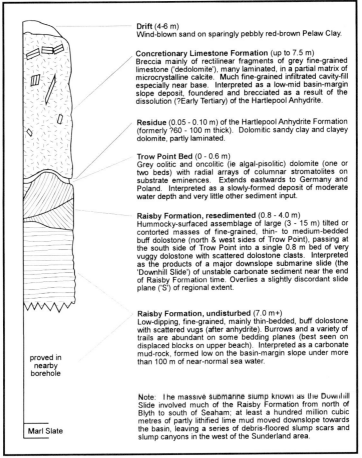

Drift (4-6 m)
Wind-blown sand on sparingly pebbly red-brown Pelaw Clay.

Concretionary Limestone Formation (up to 7.5 m)
Breccia mainly of rectilinear fragments of grey fine-grained limestone ('dedolomite'), many laminated, in a partial matrix of microcrystalline calcite. Much fine-grained infiltrated cavity-fill especially near base. Interpreted as a low-mid basin-margin slope deposit, foundered and brecciated as a result of the dissolution (?Early Tertiary) of the Hartlepool Anhydrite.

Residue (0.05 - 0.10 m) of the Hartlepool Anhydrite Formation (formerly ?60 - 100 m thick). Dolomitic sandy clay and clayey dolomite, partly laminated.

Trow Point Bed (0 - 0.6 m)
Grey oolitic and oncolitic (ie algal-pisolitic) dolomite (one or two beds) with radial arrays of columnar stromatolites on substrate eminences. Extends eastwards to Germany and Poland. Interpreted as a slowly-formed deposit of moderate water depth and very little other sediment input.

Raisby Formation, resedimented (0.8 - 4.0 m)
Hummocky-surfaced assemblage of large (3 - 15 m) tilted or contorted masses of fine-grained, thin- to medium-bedded buff dolostone (north & west sides of Trow Point), passing at the south side of Trow Point into a single 0.8 m bed of very vuggy dolostone with scattered dolostone clasts. Interpreted as the products of a major downslope submarine slide (the 'Downhill Slide') of unstable carbonate sediment near the end of Raisby Formation time. Overlies a slightly discordant slide plane ('S') of regional extent.

Raisby Formation, undisturbed (7.0 m+)
Low-dipping, fine-grained, mainly thin-bedded, buff dolostone with scattered vugs (after anhydrite). Burrows and a variety of trails are abundant on some bedding planes (best seen on displaced blocks on upper beach). Interpreted as a carbonate mud-rock, formed low on the basin-margin slope under more than 100 m of near-normal sea water.

proved in
nearby
borehole

Note: The massive submarine slump known as the Downhill Slide involved much of the Raisby Formation from north of Blyth to south of Seaham; at least a hundred million cubic metres of partly lithified lime mud moved downslope towards the basin, leaving a series of debris-floored slump scars and slump canyons in the west of the Sunderland area.

Marl Slate

Figure 13.4 Strata exposed at Trow Point.

subspherical calcite concretions with patches of inter-concretion fine-grained buff dolomite. The concretions are up to 0.25 m in diameter and most are concentrically laminated and partly coarsely radially crystalline.

Locality 5 (NZ 357576), Castletown river cliff (except at high tide); (40 mins). Wellingtons can be an advantage in approaching this exposure. Park in Sunderland Enterprise Park (NZ 35785672) and take the footpath signposted 'Hylton Riverside' to the south-southeast through a narrow wooded valley to the riverside. Here the exposure on your left comprises Yellow Sands (6 m+) resting unconformably on Upper Coal Measures sandstone (2 m+). This is the only good exposure of the unconformity in the Sunderland area; it is an almost plane erosion surface and represents a time gap of at least 40 Ma. The underlying sandstone, except for the uppermost 0.3 m, has been reddened by desert weathering and is the youngest permanently exposed Carboniferous stratum in northeast England. The Yellow Sands is a typical desert dune formation; it is weakly cemented (but with patchy well-cemented nodules) in a parallel-laminated coarse-grained basal unit (c.1 m thick) and strongly trough cross-bedded in the remainder where it is medium- to coarse-grained and almost incohesive. The sand is cut by several minor faults and fissures, some of which harbour downward-tapering brown clay probably squeezed down from the Marl Slate when the faults and fissures were created.

Locality 6 (NZ 391545) Tunstall Hills S.S.S.I. (40 mins). Approach by the track from Tunstall Road (NZ 38955464), parking at NZ 39165456 or NZ 39125452. The rock here is massive brown reef limestone of the Ford Formation and was formed near the seaward crest of the reef. It comprises a sparse framework of filter-feeding fan-like (*Fenestella*, *Synocladia*) and twiggy (*Acanthocladia*, *Dyscritella*) **bryozoans** that were fixed to the substrate or to each other, and the remains of other marine organisms (mainly bivalves, **brachiopods** and **gastropods**) that lived in the protected spaces between the bryozoans or were attached to them. High on the main face, twiggy bryozoans are thickly encrusted with concentrically finely laminated limestone that may be **algal**. Another feature of the main face is a number of steeply inclined contemporaneous tension cracks, some of which have been filled by laminated limestone whereas others have remained partly unfilled and have yielded coarse frosted wind-blown sand grains.

The ridge extending southeastwards from here is the surface

expression of the comparatively resistant reef rock; lower land to the east of the ridge corresponding with the basin which here was at least 60 m deep. The reef is more than 300 m wide, but its southwestern margin was removed during the last (i.e. late Devensian) ice age when Glacial Lake Wear overflowed southeastwards and cut the spectacular channel of Tunstall Hope.

Locality 7 (NZ 4349), Seaham S.S.S.I. (parts covered at highest tides). (60 mins, hard hats are advisable.) Park in the car park (NZ 430494) and walk via the northwest corner of North Dock (NZ 432495) and the cobbled path northwards down to the beach. Follow the beach for c. 150 m to the north-northwest, noting the industrial debris, to cliffs (NZ 43064966–43033975) where the southeast-dipping sequence is shown in Fig. 13.5. This is one of the best places in Britain for seeing an evaporite dissolution residue.

The harbour was cut into a headland of Seaham Formation limestones, which are well exposed in several large faces. Most of the limestones were originally fine-grained and thinly bedded, and many contain large numbers of *Liebea*, *Schizodus* and *Calcinema*; they are finely cross-bedded and rippled, and some are graded. Changes to some of the limestones, probably during deep burial, resulted in the creation of thick beds full of spectacular calcite concretions not unlike those at Locality 2 but without the distinctive fine lamination of the latter.

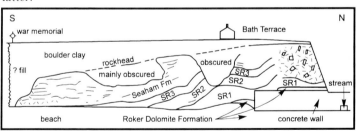

Figure 13.5 Strata exposed in the cliffs north of Seaham Harbour.
Seaham Formation (8 m+). Slightly dislocated thin- to thick-bedded mainly fine-grained buff and grey limestone with abundant *Liebea*, *Schizodus* and *Calcinema* (a small stick-like ?alga) in some beds.
SR 1–3: Seaham Residue (6–9 m). The insoluble remains of the Fordon Evaporite Formation, here otherwise dissolved. Comprises lower (SR1) and upper (SR3) units of heterogeneous calcareous clay and clayey limestone and a dislocated median unit (2m) of white to buff oolitic limestone.
Roker Dolomite Formation, top of. Cream and buff finely oolitic dolostone, partly fractured and altered to limestone.

14 · The Northern Pennine Orefield: Weardale and Nenthead

Brian Young *British Geological Survey, Edinburgh*

PURPOSE

This excursion explores the central part of the orefield. Mineralization will be seen *in situ* and in dump material. Several sites of industrial archaeological and socio-historical interest will be visited.

LOGISTICS

The excursion begins at Westgate in Weardale and ends at Nenthead, covering approximately 32 km; it is suitable for car or minibus and takes a whole day. Maximum walking distance at any one locality is less than 0.8 km. Refreshment and toilet facilities are available at Westgate, Allenheads, Killhope and Nenthead.

Note: Safety helmets are advisable. Several old mine sites will be visited. **On no account should any underground workings be entered.** Particular care should be taken in the vicinity of old shafts.

Maps

O.S. 1:50 000 Sheets 87, Hexham & Haltwhistle (Locality 1) and 92, Barnard Castle (Locations 2–8). B.G.S. 1:50 000 Sheet 25, Alston.

GEOLOGICAL BACKGROUND

The Carboniferous rocks of the Northern Pennines are cut by numerous **mineral veins**. These typically occupy normal **faults** of small vertical **throw**. A characteristic feature of the veins is their relationship to the wall-rocks. In hard rocks such as limestone and many sandstones the fault fissures are typically wide and nearly vertical; where they cut soft beds such as shale they are very narrow and inclined. Veins are therefore commonly wide and productive in hard beds and are usually barren in soft beds. Many veins are little over 1 m wide but in places widths of over 10 m have been recorded. Adjacent to some veins the chemically reactive mineralizing fluids have altered the wall-rocks, particularly limestones, giving rise to wide horizontal replacement deposits commonly rich in ore and known locally as '**flats**'.

A marked zonation of the constituent minerals within the deposits, especially the non-metalliferous or **gangue** minerals, is a striking feature of this orefield (Fig. 14.1). Deposits in the central zone carry abundant **fluorite**, commonly with **quartz**. **Chalcopyrite** is locally common near the central parts of this zone. **Galena** is most abundant towards the outer parts of the zone, where in places, workable concentrations of **sphalerite** are also present. Surrounding the fluorite zone is a wider zone of deposits in which barium minerals including **baryte** and **witherite** are the characteristic gangue. Galena and other sulphide values are commonly low in this zone.

The mineral zonation is interpreted as reflecting progressively lower temperatures of crystallization from mineralizing fluids as they flowed outwards from central 'emanative centres' above high spots (cupolas) on the underlying Weardale **Granite**. The granite may have contributed some of the elements to the deposits but its principal role in their formation is likely to have been as a heat source.

EXCURSION DETAILS

Drive north from Westgate (NY 908381) along the steep unclassified road which leads to Rookhope and park opposite an old lime kiln on the roadside adjacent to West Rigg Quarries (Fig. 14.1).

Locality 1, West Rigg Quarries (NY 911392), an **S.S.S.I.** West Rigg Quarries, on the east side of the road, provides one of the finest surface exposures of a major vein in the orefield today. The Slitt Vein forms a conspicuous vertical wall several metres wide running almost east–west through the quarries. Here it consists almost entirely of quartz with a few lenses of fluorite and only rare bands of galena. Old levels driven along galena-rich bands may be seen within the central part of the vein. Horizontal **slickensides** are present on the south face of the vein indicating lateral movement after its formation. At West Rigg the vein cuts the Great Limestone, large volumes of which have been replaced by the iron carbonate minerals **siderite** and **ankerite** during

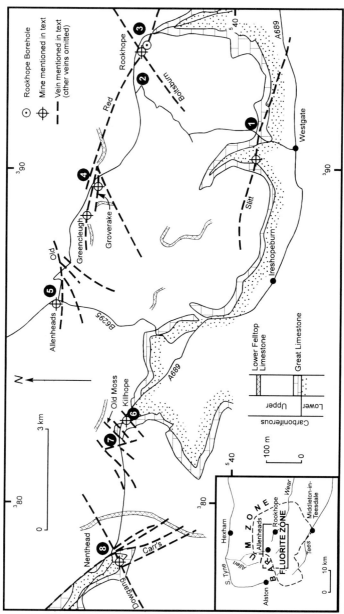

Figure 14.1 Map of the Weardale–Nenthead area showing localities mentioned in the text.

the mineralizing episode. Weathering of these to '**limonite**' produced huge deposits of iron ore which were quarried here late last century. The quarry represents the extent of these 'flats', a few remnants of which may be seen as dark brown outcrops on the quarry walls.

This quarry is best examined from the road. Immediately west of the road are further extensive opencast workings and dumps, also associated with iron ore 'flats', though little is exposed here today.

Further west across the Middlehope Valley the overgrown dumps and reservoir of Slitt Mine may be seen. Slitt Mine, from which the vein takes its name, worked galena from levels and a shaft 178 m deep sunk into the Whin **Sill**, here beneath the Tyne Bottom Limestone. Mining at Slitt ceased in 1878. Slitt Vein, one of the longest veins known in the orefield, belongs to a small group of predominantly east–west fractures known as the 'Quarter-Point' veins along which the main displacement was horizontal rather than vertical. The 'Quarter-Point' veins, including Slitt Vein, have been the main sources of fluorspar in recent years (see also Excursion 15).

Continue north along the hill road to Lintzgarth.

Locality 2, Lintzgarth (NY 925429). A short distance northwest of Lintzgarth the sole surviving arch of the Rookhope, or Lintzgarth, smelt mill chimney is conspicuous. The smelt mill itself stood immediately south of the arch. Like most Pennine lead smelters its toxic fumes were conveyed via a long horizontal flue up the fellside to a chimney on the fell top. The course of Rookhope Chimney can be followed northwest to the top of Redburn Common. Rookhope Smelt Mill processed lead ores from mines in Rookhope and Weardale operated by the Weardale Lead Company until 1919. It was the last working smelt mill in the orefield.

Turn right and drive to Rookhope Village.

Locality 3, Rookhope village (NY 937428). The shaft of the last major lead mine in the valley, the Boltsburn Mine, is situated on the south bank of Rookhope Burn opposite the village school. This mine, which worked the northeast trending Boltsburn Vein and associated 'flats' in the Great Limestone, was world famous for the magnificent fluorite cubes found in cavities of the 'flats'. Exceptionally clear crystals were exported to Austria for the manufacture of specialized lenses. The mine closed in 1931. Apart from the shaft collar and remnants of the waterwheel mountings little remains at the mine today. At least two other mines worked until recent years close to the village; their sites have been landscaped.

Close to Boltsburn shaft the Rookhope Borehole (NY 93744278) was drilled in 1960–61. This important research borehole proved the pre-Carboniferous Weardale Granite at a depth of 390.5 m at what is believed to be one of its shallowest points beneath the orefield. The granite was continuously cored to the bottom of the hole at a depth of 806 m. The bulk of the core is stored in an old mine building at Burnside Cottages immediately west of the village. Parties may arrange to visit the core store by prior arrangement with the Department of Geological Sciences, University of Durham.

Return to Rookhope Smelt Mill and drive up the road towards Allenheads. About 4.0 km along the road the surface plant of Groverake Mine will be seen to the south of the road.

Locality 4, Groverake Mine (NY 896442). Groverake and the associated mines of Frazer's **Hush** and Greencleugh are the only remaining fluorspar producers in the orefield. At Groverake at least three major veins unite but the main producer has been the east–west Groverake Vein. The outcrop of this runs between the two shafts and can be followed up the fellside east of the road as a series of collapsed **stopes** and opencasts. Purple and green fluorite are the main constituents of the Groverake Vein which is locally up to about 10 m wide. Galena values are relatively poor. Quartz and **chalcedony** are also abundant. Chalcopyrite is comparatively common here, associated in places with traces of **bismuthinite**, and microscopic amounts of **cassiterite** have also been found recently in the Groverake ore. The presence of these minerals is consistent with the view that Groverake lies above an 'emanative centre' of north Pennine mineralization.

Although developed as a moderately successful lead mine by the Beaumont Company early last century, shallow mining at Groverake probably began much earlier. It was the demand for fluorspar for metallurgical and chemical use, which arose late last century, which provided the mine with its twentieth-century success. Fluorspar mining started here in 1897 and has continued intermittently under a succession of owners. To date in excess of 700 000 tons of crude fluorspar have been produced. The oreshoot on the Groverake Vein is one of the largest known in the Pennines. It has been worked almost continuously from the Lower Felltop Limestone at the surface down to the base of the Nattrass Gill Hazle. Iron-rich 'flats', similar to those at West Rigg, were worked adjacent to the vein in the Lower Felltop Limestone east of the road.

On the south side of the valley about 1.6 km west of Groverake, other extensive iron-rich 'flats', also in the Lower Felltop Limestone, were worked both opencast and underground from the conspicuous overgrown excavations known as Frazer's Hushes (NY 884445). These flats are adjacent to the Greencleugh Vein, which is today being worked for fluorspar from the relatively new Frazer's Hush and Greencleugh mines, the former connected underground with Grove-rake Mine. A short distance west of Frazer's Hushes note the reservoir of Corbitmere Dam, one of several built last century to provide water to drive machinery at Allenheads Mine.

Continue west to Allenheads. The last 0.8 km of the road follows the valley excavated along the course of one of the main veins, the Old Vein, of Allenheads Mine. Several overgrown shaft dumps may be seen adjacent to the road.

Locality 5, Allenheads village (NY 860453) is a splendid example of a north Pennine lead mining settlement developed around the Allen-heads Mine. Many of the original mine buildings remain, including the workshop (now partly converted for use as small business premises) and numerous miners' cottages. Gin Hill Shaft, one of the main accesses to the mine, lies immediately adjacent to the road junction opposite the Allenheads Estate Office. It has recently been excavated and partly restored with a metal grille covering it. Like most mines in the orefield Allenheads relied heavily on water power. Waterwheels and other machinery both above and below ground were supplied from the numerous reservoirs on the hills around the village. A magnificent hydraulic engine built by the famous Newcastle engineer William Armstrong is preserved at the Allenheads Heritage Centre next to the Allenheads Inn.

Allenheads Mine was opened early in the eighteenth century and enjoyed a long working life, finally closing in 1896 with an estimated production of 260 000 tons of lead concentrates to its credit, making it the single most productive lead mine in the orefield. The modern stone buildings on the mine site, opposite the Inn, are all that remains of the 1970s attempt to reopen the mine for fluorspar production. This unsuccessful venture was perhaps the most expensive failure in northern Pennine mining history.

From Allenheads continue south along the B6295 road to Cowshill and then turn sharp right along the A689 to Killhope Lead Mining Centre.

Locality 6, Killhope Lead Mining Centre (NY 826430). The site of Park Level Mill and its treatment works has in recent years been restored by Durham County Council to create a most successful open-air

Figure 14.2 Restored overshot wheel, Killhope Lead Mining Centre, Weardale. *Photo*: P. Nixon.

museum. The spectacular overshot waterwheel is once again in working order (Fig. 14.2) and nineteenth century ore dressing equipment can be seen on the dressing floors. The site is today an excellent reconstruction of a nineteenth century Pennine lead mine. A visit to the museum is highly recommended. Details of the site are interpreted in excellent sign boards and leaflets, and enthusiastic staff are on hand as guides.

Leave the museum and continue west along the road. On the north side of the road west of the museum entrance is a fine exposure of the Great Limestone, one of the main host rocks for mineralization, underlain by the rather friable Tuft Sandstone.

Locality 7, Old Moss Vein (NY 820433). Old Moss Vein, one of many veins known at Killhope, is well-exposed in the Great Limestone in the bed of Killhope Burn. The vein and its altered wall-rock here carries galena, sphalerite, siderite and purple fluorite. The coral-rich Frosterley Band is exposed immediately downstream of the vein. *This site is an S.S.S.I. Please do not hammer the outcrop or attempt to collect from it.*

Continue west along the B6293 noting the superb views of Cross Fell, Great and Little Dun Fells on the southwest horizon from Killhope Cross at the Durham/Cumbria boundary.

Locality 8, Nenthead village (NY 781436). Park at the main village car park, built on the site of the Rampgill Mine dressing floors. Nenthead village was built in the eighteenth century by the London Lead Co., a Quaker company who were one of the principal mining and smelting companies in the orefield. Many veins occur in and around Nenthead and these, and numerous associated 'flats', proved extremely rich. Originally important as lead producers many of these deposits became significant sources of zinc ore in the late nineteenth and twentieth centuries. The principal zinc ore at Nenthead is sphalerite which is extremely abundant in these deposits in a zone intermediate between the fluorite and barium zones. It had hitherto been regarded as a troublesome waste product by the lead miners.

The village abounds in reminders of the heyday of lead mining. The North Pennine Heritage Trust and Cumbria County Council have recently erected interpretive signs and guide leaflets are available. Note particularly the miners' reading room, village drinking fountain, and the large building, now a bus garage, which housed a large ore-dressing plant which served several local mines. This plant recovered many tons of zinc concentrates from mine spoil during World War II. Before leaving the car park note the large wooded valley of Dowgang Hush to the south above the twin stone-arched entrances to Capel-cleugh Mine. This 'hush' is in part a man-made valley excavated by repeatedly releasing torrents of water from a dam high on the hillside to rip through the loose rock along the course of the Dowgang Vein.

Walk southeast along the track, passing the stone buildings, formerly the workshops of Rampgill Mine. Pass through the gate by a white-washed cottage and examine the well preserved assay house and smelt mill ruins. Smelting ended here late last century.

Follow the stream up to a small waterfall (NY 787429). The rock here is the Great Limestone adjacent to a north-northeast–south-southwest trending fault known as Carr's Vein. Within the northern Pennine orefield, faults with this trend are comparatively rarely mineralized and are known as 'cross veins'. In the Nenthead area, however, they clearly acted as major channels for mineralization as the Great Limestone adjacent to them is commonly altered to give extensive flat deposits which in this area carry abundant galena and sphalerite in a matrix of ankeritized limestone. The limestone here at the waterfall is a fine example of such a flat. Note the presence of galena filling cavities. The dumps from the many workings near this locality contain excellent specimens of sphalerite, galena, ankerite, quartz and calcite.

15 · Carboniferous of the Wear Valley and Derwent Gorge, County Durham

Tony Johnson *University of Durham*

PURPOSE

To examine Carboniferous (Dinantian, Namurian and Westphalian) rocks at four localities in central and northern County Durham. The spectacular gorges of the River Wear at Durham City and the River Derwent at Muggleswick are important geomorphological features.

LOGISTICS

Localities 1 (Westgate), 2 (Frosterley) and 4 (Durham City) can be reached by public transport, but Locality 3 (Derwent Gorge) is best visited by car. Parking places are available at all localities. With transport, Localities 1, 2 and 3 can be visited in one day; Locality 4 will require an extra half day. Walking distance depends on the routes taken, but is not more than 4.5 km at Locality 1, 2 km at Locality 2, 4.5 km at Locality 3 and 1.5 km at Locality 4.

Prior permission for access to Harehope Quarry (Locality 2) should be obtained from Mr R. J. Huddleston, Tilcon Ltd, P.O. Box 5, Fell Bank, Birtley, Chester-le-Street, Durham, DH3 2ST, and for access to the Derwent Gorge (Locality 3A) from the Site Manager (Tel: 0191 586 0004).

Maps

O.S. 1:50 000 Sheets 87 Hexham & Haltwistle, 88 Tyneside & Durham, 92 Barnard Castle; B.G.S. 1:50 000 Sheets 20 Newcastle upon Tyne, 25 Alston, 26 Wolsingham; B.G.S. 1:63 360 Sheet 27 Durham.

GEOLOGICAL BACKGROUND

The Carboniferous rocks of County Durham **dip** eastwards off the northern Pennines so that the Lower Carboniferous (Dinantian) crops out in the west followed by successively higher Namurian and Westphalian (Coal Measures) strata towards the east. Permian sediments overlie the Coal Measures in east Durham. Bedrock is masked by thick glacial **drift** in the eastern part of the county and natural exposures of the Coal Measures are relatively few and incomplete. Further west, the Namurian sequence forms the tops of the fells in west Durham and here almost continuous blanket bog limits the exposures of bedrock. The Dinantian crops out in the valleys of the Pennines where it can be seen in river and stream sections. Thick and continuous Dinantian limestone successions in southern England and the Midlands change northwards into sequences of limestone, shale and sandstone in northern England as the Carboniferous shoreline is approached. The most northerly of the thick Asbian limestones, the Melmerby Scar Limestone, becomes divided by clastic sediment and looses its identity in Durham. Clastic sediment increases in the overlying Brigantian where cyclic deposition of limestone, shale and sandstone is repeated ten times. This **Yoredale** facies is remarkably persistent over northern England from the Scottish Border southwards to the Craven **faults**. The sequence is controlled to an extent by the position of the Carboniferous shoreline. Marine limestones and shales increase in thickness seawards towards the south and west and thin and die out towards the shore to the north and east. Similarly, the deltaic and subaerial sandstones and coal seams thicken landwards and thin seawards. Durham lies almost midway across the broad area in which open sea and shoreline environments alternated and well developed **cyclothems** of marine and deltaic sediment are developed. A section of Yoredale cycles in Middlehope Burn is described at Locality 1.

The Great Limestone (22 m) is the thickest limestone in the Yoredale succession. It contains fossil **biostromes** including the Frosterley Marble, a band rich in solitary rugose **corals** (Locality 2). Index fossils collected from above and below the limestone indicate that the base lies near to the Dinantian/Namurian boundary. The Great Limestone cycle continues the Yoredale facies into the Namurian, but above this the limestone bands become thinner in a dominantly shale and sandstone succession. Towards the top of the Namurian thick, coarse-grained sandstones are widely developed. The upper part of the Namurian including the First and Second Grits

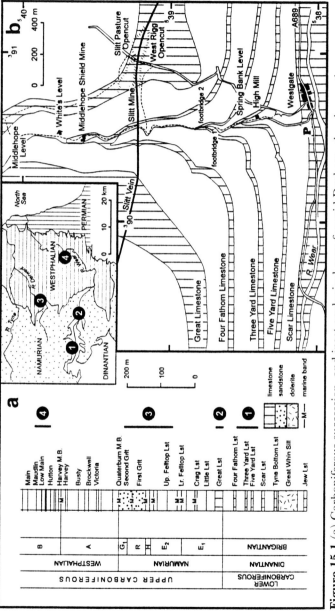

Figure 15.1 (a) Carboniferous succession, and inset geological map for mid Durham, showing sections described at localities 1–4. (b) Geology of Middlehope Burn, Westgate (Locality 1).

can be seen at Locality 3.

In Durham the base of the Westphalian is believed to be at the level of the Quarterburn Marine Band. The upper Namurian coarse-grained sandstone facies continues into the Westphalian and rapidly gives way to a delta-top sequence of sandstone and shale with coal seams. These deposits, formed mainly in lakes and interdistributary bays, contain twenty major exploitable coal seams that formed the celebrated Northumberland and Durham coalfield. A Westphalian B succession can be seen at Locality 4.

EXCURSION DETAILS

Locality 1, Middlehope Burn, Westgate, Upper Weardale. The area is a botanical **S.S.S.I.** with access by footpath, but the land is private. Upper Weardale is reached by the A689 from Crook in the east or from Alston in the west. Buses (Weardale Motor Services) travel up the dale from Crook and Bishop Auckland.

At Westgate park in the lay-by on the north side of the road just west of the centre of the village (NY 906380). Take the road to Rookhope north from the middle of the village and after 300 m turn left on the footpath past High Mill and along the side of Middlehope Burn (Fig. 15.1). The stream gives fairly continuous exposures of Dinantian Yoredale cyclothems in the upper part of the Brigantian Stage. Sandstone and interbedded shale high in the Scar Cyclothem can be seen in the stream at the mill and it forms waterfalls up stream.

The Five Yard Limestone crops out above this sequence and forms a wide series of exposures in the bed of the stream (NY 907385). Spring Bank level on the right of the path is the drainage level of Slitt Mine. Shale and sandstone above the limestone can be seen in the stream with the thicker Six Fathom Hazle well exposed in waterfalls at the first bridge across the stream. Just above the second bridge the Three Yard Limestone crops out in the sides of the stream and the succession of shales and sandstone above the limestone can be seen up stream to Slitt Mine (NY 906392). Slitt Mine shaft lies on the west side of the stream and is capped by steel plates. It was sunk to 178 m, reaching the base of the Great Whin **Sill** here intruded into the Tyne Bottom Limestone. The mine worked Slitt Vein between 1818 and 1880 and produced around 100 000 tons of lead ore (Dunham, 1990). Small amounts of **galena**, **siderite** and **fluorite** can be found on the dumps and washing floors adjacent to the shaft. Although the mine buildings have long disappeared, level entrances, waterwheel pits, engine mountings, and bingsteads etc. can still be seen.

From Slitt Mine a path leads eastwards up the valley side past Slitt Pasture opencut to the Westgate-Rookhope road at West Rigg opencut (NY 911392). This is a shorter route that cuts out the higher part of the Middlehope Burn section.

Continuing up Middlehope Burn, the Nattrass Gill Hazle sandstone at the top of the Three Yard Cyclothem is well exposed above the path and shortly up stream the Four Fathom Limestone can be seen above the sandstone. The limestone crops out at path level a little further on. Extensive old buildings beyond this are all that remains of a waterwheel crushing mill and washing floors of Middlehope Shield Mine. Old dams and lagoons are still visible. White's Level, on the east of the stream at the top of the washing floors, is one of the mine entrances. Another entrance is Middlehope Level further up stream at NY 904402. This mine produced some 15 800 tons of lead ore between 1818 and 1864 from veins to the east of the burn (Dunham, 1990).

Take the track east from Middlehope Level and turn right after a short distance on to a farm track that leads to the road at West Rigg opencut on Slitt Vein (NY 911392) (Excursion 14). Return to Westgate down the hill by the road.

Locality 2, Harehope Quarry and Bollihope Burn, near Frosterley, Weardale. Access by footpaths only across private land. Travel by the A689 to Frosterley and park at the turning south, 700 m east of the village centre (NZ 035369). Cross the River Wear by the bridge and the railway by the level crossing and turn left on the road to Broadwood (NZ 038366). South of Broadwood a stile on the right of the road leads to a track running southwest near to the side of Harehope Quarry. The quarry shows fine sections of the Great Limestone and the overlying beds, but is private and permission to enter must be obtained in advance (see Logistics).

Proceed up the track to a quarry spoil tip at the crest of the slope and turn left on a footpath that leads to Wise Eel Bridge over Bollihope Burn (NZ 034361). Turn right, cross Harehope Burn by the bridge and continue up the side of Bollihope Burn on the footpath to the first field boundary wall (NZ 03153605). Here the Great Limestone forms natural outcrops in the stream and the Frosterley Marble band, containing many solitary rugose corals, mainly *Dibunophyllum bipartitum*, is well exposed on bedding planes and in sections. Permission has been given by the landowner for access to the stream section from the footpath. *Do not damage the outcrop by hammering and collecting*; loose fragments of Frosterley Marble can be found in the stream bed below the exposures. Return to Frosterley by the same route.

Locality 3, the Derwent Gorge, Muggleswick to Shotley Bridge. From Frosterley travel east to Wolsingham, turn left on the A68 at NZ 131355 and go north through Tow Law. At Castleside turn left again on a minor road to Healeyfield and first right for the Derwent Gorge.

Locality 3A, The Derwent Gorge and associated Muggleswick Woods, containing areas of ancient oak-birch-ash woodland, form an extensive National Nature Reserve run by English Nature. Prior permission for access is required (see Logistics). The River Derwent forms incised meanders east of Muggleswick with steep or precipitous sides deeply cut into the upper Namurian bedrock. Much of the gorge is heavily forested, but there is access by a footpath that crosses the river at Lead Mill Bridge (NZ 054488). On the south side of the gorge the footpath starts beside the road at NZ 05444877 where there is limited parking beside large wooden gates. The site manager may be able to offer parking at Crooked Oak (NZ 05504976) which is at the north end of the footpath. Follow the footpath into the gorge and note sporadic exposures of upper Namurian sandstone and shale. The slopes above the river are much affected by landslips, but several bedrock sections are visible either at or above the Upper Felltop Limestone. A short way down stream a high cliff beside the river at NZ 058492 shows a fine succession of interbedded sandstone and shale with calcareous beds including limestone, assigned to the Upper Felltop, 10 m below the top of the section. The sequence shows rapid lateral variation. A section of strata here is appended to the Geological Survey six-inch sheet NZ 04 NE. This cliff section is one of the best continuous exposures of upper Namurian strata in this region. A short distance down stream ruins of buildings and an old shaft mark the site of Silvertongue Mines where lead ore was extracted from north-trending veins in the 1840s (Durham, 1990).

Locality 3B, Allensford, a County Geological Site; access by footpath only. Return to the A68 and proceed to Allensford. Take the Consett road just south of Allensford bridge and after a short distance turn left into the picnic area car park (NZ 078502). Walk back and cross the A68 to the marked footpath that starts between houses and runs up stream beside the River Derwent. Cross the Warnley Burn by the footbridge where a fine view of the thick Durham First Grit (upper Namurian) can be seen with waterfalls and a steep sided incised channel. Further up stream the grit forms the striking vertical cliffs of Ravens Crag, more that 10 m high, where massive coarse-grained and pebbly, **cross-bedded** sandstones are well exposed.

Locality 3C, Shotley Bridge, County Geological Site; access by footpaths. From Allensford car park, turn left along the minor road to Consett. Turn left at the junction with the A691, continue to the bottom of the hill and turn sharply left into Shotley Grove Road (NZ 090524); limited parking is available beside the road. The River Derwent has cut a sharply incised channel into the Durham Second Grit (upper Namurian) from Shotley Grove down stream to the B6287 road bridge over the river in the centre of Shotley Bridge. The shallow, almost vertical-sided gorge can be seen at many places on both sides of the river, but is best viewed from the foot bridge (NZ 089523). The brown, coarse-grained, cross-bedded standstone is best examined at the south end of the section near to Shotley Grove.

Although only two coarse-grained sandstone bands are distinguished at the top of the Namurian in the Derwent valley, elsewhere in County Durham three or even four grit bands are present in this part of the succession.

Locality 4, the River Wear Gorge at Durham City; Coal Measures, Westphalian B (Johnson & Richardson, 1990). Access is by path through woodland owned mainly by the Dean and Chapter of Durham and Durham University. There are car parks near Durham city centre, but during the university vacations it is convenient to park in Quarry Heads Lane on the south side of the river (NZ 27304154) (Fig. 15.2). Cross the road and walk east towards the New Inn. Before the traffic lights a footpath on the edge of playing fields leads to the wooded banks of the River Wear. Descend towards the river and take the first footpath on the right over the stream by a small bridge. Above the path (A) is the Maudlin Sandstone overlying the thin Maudlin Coal (Figs. 15.1, 15.2). Continue on this path to St Oswald's Church where it joins the lower path on the river bank. A short distance back along the lower path, a narrow way leads down the river bank to St Oswald's Well (B) where the Maudlin Sandstone is exposed in a low cliff. The well is at the base of the sandstone and the thin Maudlin Coal can be seen at water level with clay **seatearth** below. Inter-bedded sandstone and shale are exposed under the wellhead. Continue down the river by the lower path to the white bridge (C) where the Maudlin and underlying Low Main Post sandstones can be seen. Behind the bridge a conduit drains the abandoned pumping shaft of Elvet Landsale Colliery, marked by a ring of masonry 50 m south of the bridge. Near the bridge two small faults take the Maudlin Sandstone to the top of the river bank on the west (Fig. 15.2). A short distance further down river the Low Main Post Sandstone can be seen beside the path in an old quarried section. Past the next tributary stream, take the path up the river bank and the first path on the right to the flat wooded top of the bank. Another circle of masonry here marks the site of the shaft of Henry Pit, an early 19th century colliery working the Hutton Coal on the south side of the river. Follow the path

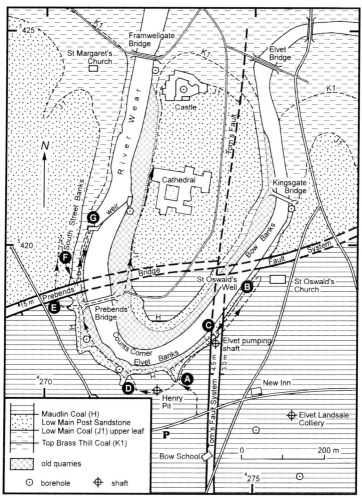

Figure 15.2 Geological map of the River Wear Gorge, Durham City. Details of boreholes are given in Johnson and Richardson (1990).

to the steep descent down the river bank (D) where the brown Maudlin Sandstone and succession below are well exposed and the Low Main Post can be seen low down on the other side of the gulley. These ancient sandstone quarries date from mediaeval times; one that worked both the Maudlin and the Low Main Post sandstones can be seen a little further along the path.

At Prebends' Bridge, the brown Maudlin Sandstone with conspicuous cross-bedding is seen in the track side leading to the bridge with the Maudlin Coal below the overhang at the base of the sandstone. A blocked **adit** entrance above the sandstone exposure is a drainage level from another early 19th century colliery. Slightly north, the Prebends' Bridge Fault, **downthrowing** 15 m south, crosses the gorge (Fig. 15.2) and steeply dipping sandstone adjacent to the fault can be seen above the path to the right of the drainage level (E). On the north side of the fault all the Low Main Post Sandstone has been quarried at the top of the river bank leaving a hollow below South Street (F). Traces of the Low Main Coal, 0.45 m thick, are found below the quarry. Extensive exposures of shale and sandstone beside the mill (G) on the left bank of the river are near the Brass Thill coals, and the Brass Thill Shell Bed can be found in the shale.

On the right bank of the river, ancient quarrying for sandstone has been extensive from Framwellgate Bridge almost continuously to Elvet Bridge and these old workings are now deeply buried in spoil and rubbish (Fig. 15.2). The Low Main Post Sandstone is seen directly below the City Wall and the Galilee Chapel, beside the high path under the Cathedral. This sandstone, 10 m thick, has been the sure foundation of the Cathedral for 900 years.

16 · The geology and landscape of Upper Teesdale

John Senior *University of Durham*

PURPOSE

To study the Carboniferous **cyclothemic** sediments on the edge of the Caledonian Alston Block; the **Variscan tectonics**, Whin **Sill** and synchronous mineralisation; the Tertiary Cleveland **Dyke**; the effects of late Quaternary glaciation and the control of landscape by the underlying geology. Parts of the sequence are very fossiliferous, with **corals**, **crinoids** and **brachiopods.**

LOGISTICS

A one-day excursion which may profitably be divided into smaller, more intensive itineraries. Parking places are indicated throughout the text. Food may be obtained in Middleton-in-Teesdale, at High Force and at Holwick.

Note: Although the paths are recognized rights of way they pass through two large estates (Raby and Strathmore). Please observe the countryside code. During the pheasant and grouse shooting seasons, sections of the proposed routes may be temporarily closed.

Maps

O.S. 1:50 000 Sheet 92, Barnard Castle; O.S. 1:25 000 Sheet NY 82/92, Middleton-in-Teesdale; B.G.S. 1:50 000 Sheet 31, Brough-under-Stainmoor; B.G.S. 1:63 360 Sheet 32 Barnard Castle; B.G.S. 1:25 000 Sheet 17, Middleton-in-Teesdale.

GEOLOGICAL BACKGROUND

Upper Teesdale is situated on the southern margin of the Alston Block, part of a structural block and trough system developed in

Northern England following the **Caledonian Orogeny**. The foundation of the block in the Teesdale area comprises Ordovician **metasediments** (exposed in the Teesdale **inlier** at Cronkley Pasture; NY 846296) and **volcaniclastic** deposits (Borrowdale Volcanic Group) into which the Weardale **Granite** has been emplaced.

This buoyant structural unit is bounded on its southern margin by the Lunedale–Butterknowle **Fault** zone, separating it from the Stainmore Trough, a substantial depositional basin during the Carboniferous period. In the subsiding Stainmore Trough some 2850 m of cyclic Carboniferous sediments are still preserved; equivalent strata on the more stable Alston Block are appreciably thinner. In Teesdale and adjacent areas each Yoredale cyclothem commences with a marine **transgression** (usually a limestone which gives a generic name to the whole unit; e.g. Five Yard Limestone Cyclothem) followed by sediments of increasing deltaic influence (shales, siltstones, flagstones, sandstones or grits, **seatearths** and perhaps thin coals). The terrestrially derived sediments represent the infilling of a shallow marine gulf by a southerly **prograding** deltaic complex. The number of such Yoredale cyclothems in the North Pennine area suggests that sedimentary basin infill was followed by regional subsidence and/or increase in sea-level, with many repetitions of the sedimentary cycle over many millions of years.

The end-Carboniferous Variscan Orogeny led to reactivation of basement faults and general uplift of the Northern Pennines area. A late orogenic extensional phase resulted in the injection of basic **magma** into deep-seated fault zones, some of which acted as feeder dykes for the extensive Whin Sill, a very important **doleritic** intrusion in North East England. Upper Teesdale, the southern limit of this **igneous** body, was where the intrusive nature of a sill was first recognized by Adam Sedgwick in 1827. The important Northern Pennines mineralization is chronologically associated with this re-heating of the basement rocks of the block areas by these basic magmas (Dunham 1990). **Mineral veins** (base metals lead, zinc and iron with a little copper, silver and cobalt) are to be found in fault zones cutting the Carboniferous sediments and indeed replacing some of the limestones in particular. The legacy of intensive mining in the past litters the Teesdale landscape.

Post-Variscan faulting in the Teesdale area is complicated by subsequent tectonic episodes (Triassic, intra-Jurassic, early Tertiary and even late Quaternary **eustatic** movements) so many faults show different phases and directions of movement and there are some cases of fault inversion. Into one such fault zone were injected basic magmas believed to have originated from the early Tertiary (Palaeocene) Mull volcanic centre. This Cleveland-Armathwaite Dyke **echelon** is well represented in Upper Teesdale.

Only features associated with the latest Quaternary (Devensian) glaciation are represented in Upper Teesdale but these have had a profound effect. Much of the landscape is masked by deposits of **till** which is of local (Pennine) origin except in the Lunedale and Middleton-in-Teesdale area where distinctive glacial **erratics** of Shap Granite and green **andesitic tuffs** (Borrowdale Volcanic Group) witness the passage of Lake District ice through the Stainmore pass and Lunedale area onto the South Durham–North Yorkshire plains. Geomorphological features in Upper Teesdale suggest a late Quaternary valley glacier phase with marginal **moraines**, linear ice moulded debris, glacial **spillways** and modified river patterns, as well as outwash sand and gravel deposits which choke the Tees valley.

EXCURSION DETAILS

Locality 1, Eggleston Burn (NY 989252). Approach from Eggleston village via either the B6282 (Middleton-in-Teesdale road) or B6278 (Stanhope road) and the linking minor road (Fig. 16.2). Park on the roadside (NY 990249), 150 m east of the spectacular gritstone viaduct across Eggleston Burn. Walk along the narrow path on the north side of the road (just to the east of the viaduct) for 100 m to a small ill-defined quarry. Here the Cleveland Dyke crosses the valley and burn in an east–west direction, emplaced into coarse **feldspathic** gritstones around the level of the Firestone Sill (Upper Carboniferous). The **porphyritic tholeiitic** dolerite of this minor intrusion has been modestly quarried on the east side of the burn for roadstone (trackways lead southwards from the lower section near the burn) and there are signs that the adjacent grits have also been quarried for local walling.

The full c.15 m thickness of the dyke is best seen in the river cliff on the west side of the valley, where it has chilled (**tachylitic**) margins and the adjacent grits have been mildly contact **metamorphosed**. It is, however, difficult from a distance to distinguish the sedimentary bedding of the host rock from the horizontal **joints** of the dyke. In the quarry on the east side of the burn the marginal contacts are not well exposed, but the quarry face does exhibit good examples of spheroidal weathering in the dyke.

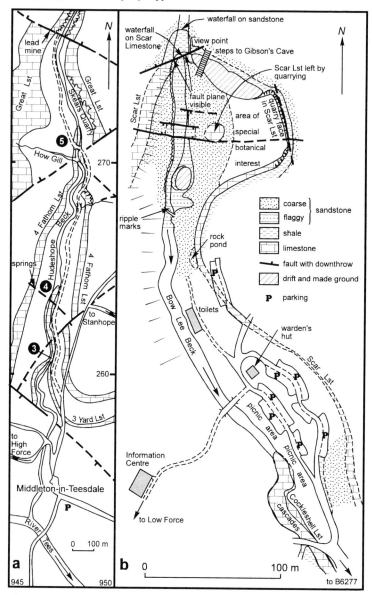

Figure 16.1 (a) Geological map and localities in Hudeshope Beck, Middleton-in-Teesdale. (b) Geology of Bowlees Quarry and picnic area.

Locality 2, Whistle Crag (NY 978247). From the lay-by on the B6282 is a panoramic view southwards of the southern marginal area of the Alston Block. Crags of Whin Sill can be seen below the skyline to the right, whilst the Lunedale–Butterknowle Fault runs just below the skyline on the left and out through the Lune Valley to the south. The Tees valley in the foreground is filled by late Quaternary tills and outwash alluvial deposits.

Localities 3–5, Hudeshope Beck (NY 947258–948275). Park in Middleton-in-Teesdale. Walk north from the town on the Stanhope road past the parish chruch. Viewed from the wall on the west side of the road after the last house, the disturbed limestones at river level mark the position where a fault (**downthrowing** to the southwest) cuts the deep valley of Hudeshope Beck. Take the first pathway on the west side of the road through the woods on the east side of the beck to the first footbridge.

Locality 3 (NY 947258). The footbridge is sited on the thickest **post** of the Three Yard Limestone (Lower Carboniferous, Alston Group) where it also forms a small waterfall (Fig. 16.1a). Downstream the base of the limestone is exposed where it overlies the sandstones, **ganister** and thin shale partings at the top of the Five Yard Limestone Cyclothem. In the low river cliffs on the east side of the valley upstream of the footbridge a sequence of thin limestones with intercalated calcareous shales (with scattered corals and crinoidal debris) is gradually replaced vertically by deltaic non-marine shales with ironstone nodules followed by flaggy sandstones, all part of the Three Yard Limestone Cyclothem.

Further upstream the sandstone of the Three Yard Limestone Cyclothem forms a low river cliff. This disappears where a fault (the continuation of the Holm Head Vein), downthrowing c.10 m southeast, cuts the valley in a northeast–southwest direction and results in the repetition of the geological succession so that the second footbridge (NY 947262) is also sited on the thickest post of the Three Yard Limestone. Around the second footbridge, a c.0.4 m bed of calcareous shale separates the two principal posts of the Three Yard Limestone. As the river bed gradient is the same as the local **dip** the stream bed follows the top of the limestone for 150 m upstream where a small fault causes flexure in the top of the upper post.

Locality 4 (NY 947264). A series of **tufa**-depositing springs are associated with this same fault on the western side of the valley. A large mound of tufa from a former lower spring source is known locally as the 'Growing Stone' (Fig. 16.1a).

The calcareous shales upstream provide many well preserved examples of crinoid sections, brachiopods, **bryozoan** colonies and occasional fish teeth. Among boulder debris in the beck are examples of exotic clasts derived from the till cover in this valley, including green andesitic volcaniclastic rocks (Borrowdale Volcanic Group) and Shap Granite from the Lake District, as well as locally derived material including clasts of Frosterley Marble.

Further upstream (NY 948269) the nature of the Three Yard Limestone Cyclothem changes with non-marine ferruginous shales with **septarian sideritic** nodules followed by siltstones, flagstones then a more substantial sandstone that forms the lip of a prominent waterfall.

Walking up the Hudeshope valley along the road, the limestones of the succeeding Four Fathom Limestone Cyclothem have been worked in a rather overgrown quarry (NY 949269) and although somewhat disrupted by faulting these same limestones can be seen forming low cliffs on the west bank of the beck (Fig. 16.1a).

Locality 5 (NY 948272). The Four Fathom Limestone is extensively exposed in the river bed upstream of Skears Bridge, where it is also markedly disrupted by **calcite**-filled tension gashes associated with mineralized faulting. Higher upstream, the sedimentary sequence between the Four Fathom Limestone and the Great Limestone (Namurian, Upper Carboniferous) is seen in a poorly accessible west-facing river cliff. At Skears Scars (NY 948276) Hudeshope Beck has cut a spectacular gorge through the Great Limestone which commences on the north side at a well exposed partly mineralized fault with 18 m downthrow to the northeast (Hall's Vein; Fig. 16.1a). Beds here and in nearby Skears Quarry (NY 949272), rich in the solitary coral *Dibunophyllum bipartitum*, constitute the Frosterley Marble horizon.

Return to the vehicle and leave Middleton-in-Teesdale on the B6277 for Bowlees.

Locality 6, Bowlees Picnic site (NY 907283). Around the old limestone quarry (NY 908284) there is a wealth of geological detail (summarized on Fig. 16.1b) which requires careful observation.

Walk upstream on the well-made path from the quarry. Above the quarry fault waterfall, Bow Lee Beck runs over the **cross-bedded** and channel fill sandstones of the Scar Limestone Cyclothem the top of

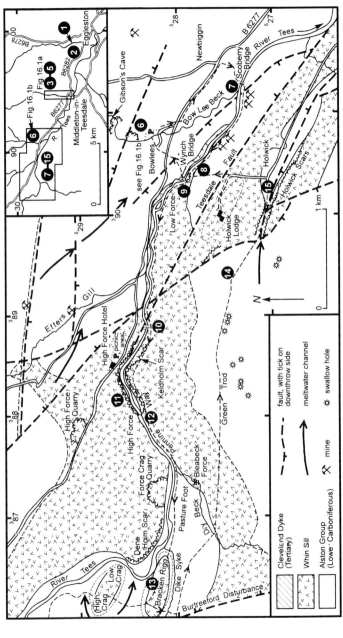

Figure 16.2 Geological map of upper Teesdale around High Force. Inset showing localities described in text.

which is at Gibson's Cave (NY 910287) where the limestones of the succeeding Five Yard Limestone Cyclothem form the lip of the waterfall.

Leave the picnic area and walk eastwards on the B6277 for 0.6 km before taking the footpath southwest to the River Tees (Fig. 16.2).

Locality 7, Scoberry Bridge (NY 910273). Here the Cockleshell Limestone is exposed with the brachiopod *Gigantoproductus* and compound corals (do not hammer this locality). Cross the bridge and walk upstream on the Pennine Way. The gentle downstream dip brings in successively lower strata of the Single Post Limestone Cyclothem and into the top of the Tyne Bottom Limestone Cyclothem. Note the waste heaps from Wynch Mine trials into the Single Post Limestone (iron and zinc replacement ores) to the southwest side of the path some 300–550 m upstream from the bridge (Dunham 1990).

The River Tees changes its character some 200 m upstream from the bridge, caused by the exposure of the top margin of the Whin Sill. The sill has been injected into the sandstones of the Tyne Bottom Limestone Cyclothem and now forms the bed of the River Tees for 1.7 km upstream to Holwick Head Bridge (NY 889283). The indurate nature of the upper margin of the Whin Sill causes the river to flow over a series of rapids, small waterfalls and through small sharply defined valleys.

Locality 8 (NY 904278). Here there is a large 2–2.5 m thick raft of metamorphosed sandstone in the upper part of the Whin Sill. This 74 m long section of detached roof rock has tilted to an angle of c.20° as it slowly foundered into the crystallising basic magmatic intrusion, producing glassy tachylitic chilled margins to the edge of the sill and in turn being metamorphosed.

Locality 9, Wynch Bridge (NY 903280). Cross over the nineteenth century bridge to view Low Force, a well loved river feature effected by the hard nature and crude columnar jointing of the Whin Sill. Pause on the bridge to note the full extent of the sandstone raft at Locality 8. (The walk can be terminated here. Return to the Bowlees Picnic area, noting in passing the long low, partly wooded hill to the east of the path at the start of the fields: a northwest–southeast oriented, extended, ice moulded heap of glacial debris.)

Walking upriver on the west bank from Wynch Bridge, many features associated with the erosion of the upper contact of the Whin

Sill can be noted in the river course. Also the wet nature of the associated valley alluvial deposits makes this section of Teesdale an ideal area for the study of summer wetland plants.

Locality 10, Holwick Head Bridge (NY 889283). Here the nature of the Tees valley changes where the river enters a deeply incised gorge which terminates with the waterfall of High Force (NY 880284). Near this bridge the river crosses a major north-northwest–south-southeast fault complex which has the combined effect of some c.75 m downthrow to the east (Fig. 16.2). Indeed the continuation of the Teesdale Fault controls the northwest–southeast direction of the first section of the High Force Gorge.

This locality may also be approached from the public car park and picnic site at High Force (NY 886287).

Locality 11, High Force (NY 881284). Park as above and take the woodland walks and paths maintained by the Raby Estate to the waterfall. This approach will allow you to see at close hand the bottom section of the Whin Sill where the quartz dolerite magma has been injected into the sandstones of the Tyne Bottom Limestone Cyclothem (again the bottom contact of the sill has a chilled tachylitic margin). The disposition of the rock types viewed at this classic locality can be seen in Fig. 16.3.

Figure 16.3 High Force (Locality 11). WS = Whin Sill; S = metamorphosed sandstone; TBL = Tyne Bottom Limestone. *Photo:* J. Senior.

Continuing upstream on the west bank from Holwick Head Bridge, the path ascends a steep slope to a position about halfway up the Whin Sill intrusion, some 73 m thick in this area. The well defined path passes through preserved areas of juniper scrub, remnant areas of woody plant colonisation left after the last, Devensian, glaciation. There are several places where ***with extreme caution*** High Force can be viewed from the rim of the gorge.

Locality 12, Top of High Force (NY 880284). Views of the waterfall and the gorge beyond are spectacular and ***dangerous***. Flash floods generated by summer storms in the Pennines often surprise the unwary at this locality.

Following the Pennine Way upstream, Bleabeck Force is seen to cascade over the Whin Sill on the south side of the valley (NY 875278) and on the north side of the Tees there is the active Force Garth Quarry. Here almost the whole thickness of the Whin Sill (often showing working faces with excellent columnar jointing) is worked for roadstone.

The low and ill-drained ground around Pasture Foot (Fig. 16.2) is part of a pre-glacial buried channel now partly choked by till.

Locality 13, Bracken Rigg (NY 863281). The Pennine Way ascends this small but steep hill, an erosional **outlier** of dolerite, that with Low Crag to the north (NY 863287) has become detached from the main outcrop of the Whin Sill by post-glacial erosion of the River Tees. The south-facing columnar dolerite cliffs of Dene Holm Scar and the adjacent Tees valley are a splendid sight from the top of Bracken Rigg. Leave the Pennine Way at the western end of Bracken Rigg and walk southwards across the marshy ground of Fell Dike Sike (a continuation of the Pasture Foot buried channel) to join the well defined drove road 'Green Trod'. This possibly Iron Age trans-Pennine routeway can now be followed eastwards across the grouse moors to Holwick. Green Trod follows the Scar Limestone Cyclothem sediments above the Whin Sill and many swallow holes may be seen developed in the Scar Limestone.

Locality 14, Low Currick Rigg (NY 895275). Below lies the dour gritstone Royal hunting lodge, Holwick House, prominently situated on top of a northwest–southeast elongated ice-moulded mound of glacial debris (one of many such glacial features in this part of Teesdale). On the skyline to the northeast is Coldberry Gutter, a man-made 30 m deep valley which cuts the watershed. This prominent feature is a '**hush**', produced by mining and repeated flushing which removed some 2.5 million tonnes of waste in the 17th–19th centuries to produce lead ore concentrate.

Locality 15, Holwick (NY 901271). Fine cliffs of columnar dolerite form Holwick Scars and Crossthwaite Scars. These and the side valleys are probably fault controlled (Fig. 16.2), but accentuated by the Devensian glaciation of the valley margin, which also accounts for the modified drainage, glacial deposits and periglacial scree slopes at the foot of these north-facing cliffs (Fig. 16.4).

Walking northwards from Holwick Scars to Low Force (Locality 9) the route passes over two and possibly three faults of the Teesdale Fault complex, with a composite downthrow to the north of c.100 m.

Figure 16.4 The Whin Sill forming Howick Scars, looking east (Locality 15). *Photo:* J. Senior.

17 · The Carboniferous and Permian rocks in southern County Durham

Trevor Morse *University of Durham* and
Denys Smith *GEOPERM & University of Durham*

PURPOSE

To examine the Carboniferous and Permian rocks, and the Tertiary Cleveland **Dyke**, of the lower Tees valley and adjoining areas, southern County Durham.

LOGISTICS

The complete excursion occupies two days but can be split conveniently into shorter sections. A vehicle is essential because the localities are widely spaced (Fig. 17.1). Cars can be parked at or near the roadside, and all roads are suitable for small coaches. Localities 1 and 2 involve up to 3 km walking on paths and rough ground in the Butterknowle and Cockfield Fell area. Localities 3–10 entail a total of up to 10 km walking along riverside paths of the Tees and Greta between Barnard Castle and Piercebridge, finishing at a quarry at High Coniscliffe (Locality 11). The excursion has been ordered for convenience of travel but could be rearranged in geological sequence to finish with Localities 1, 2, 10 and 11 (Fig. 17.3). It would be best undertaken in early spring, when vegetation least masks outcrops and views.

Barnard Castle has pubs, public toilets, shops, restaurants and buildings of historical interest. Most of the other localities are near to villages with pubs and shops.

Note: If the Rivers Tees and Greta are in flood, this excursion should not be attempted.

Maps

O.S. 1:25 000 sheets NZ 02/12 Woodland & West Auckland, NZ 01/11 Barnard Castle & Gainford, NZ 21/31 Darlington; O.S. 1:50 000

sheets 92 Barnard Castle, 93 Middlesbrough & Darlington; B.G.S.
1:63 360 Sheet 32 Barnard Castle (solid and drift editions).

GEOLOGICAL BACKGROUND

The area is dominated by the Carboniferous rocks on the northern
flank of the broad, open Middleton Tyas **Anticline**, an east–west
striking **Variscan** structure (Fig. 17.2) within the Stainmore Trough.
The major subdivisions of the Carboniferous form three distinct east–
west belts across the excursion area, generally **dipping** and younging
towards the north (Fig. 17.1). Dinantian rocks occupy the core of the
anticline south of the River Tees (Barnard Castle to Piercebridge), the
Namurian a central area from the River Tees to the north side of
Langleydale, and the coal-bearing Westphalian rocks in the north
form the southern edge of the Durham coalfield.

The Carboniferous succession is dominated by numerous repetitions of lithological sequences, called **cyclothems**, which change in
character from dominantly marine in the Dinantian to fluvio-
lacustrine in the Westphalian. This cyclicity reflects **eustatic** rise
and fall of sea level, probably driven by an extended period of
glaciation in polar regions, locally modified by **tectonic** and sedimentological effects. Dinantian **lithologies** are characterized by thick
marine limestones, shales and sandstones, so called **Yoredale** cyclothems. During the Namurian, fluvial systems **prograded** from the
northeast and east, resulting in the increasing dominance of medium
to coarse-grained, usually **cross-bedded** sandstones. By Westphalian
times, a vast floodplain had developed, with deltaic complexes
building out into lakes and frequent episodes of soil formation with the
development of a rich, tropical vegetation. These Coal Measures
cycles consist of inter-distributary sands, silts and muds with well
developed **seatearths** and coals, cut by medium-grained channel
sandstones. Marine influence is limited to occasional thin bands of
shales with marine fossils.

Following the Variscan Orogeny and a prolonged period of late
Carboniferous and early Permian erosion, the Permian sequence, now
dipping gently eastwards, **unconformably oversteps** successively
lower units of the Carboniferous to the south. The fine-grained
dolostone of the late Permian Raisby Formation (formerly the Lower
Magnesian Limestone) is succeeded by the **oolitic** dolostone of the
Ford Formation (formerly the Middle Magnesian Limestone).
Younger Permian and Mesozoic rocks lie beyond the eastern margin
of the area. During the early Tertiary the **tholeiitic** Cleveland Dyke,

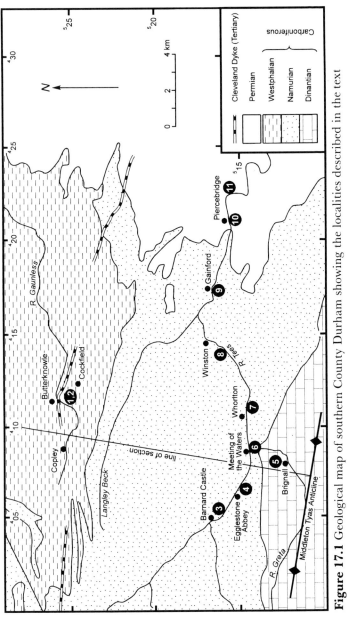

Figure 17.1 Geological map of southern County Durham showing the localities described in the text (after Mills & Hull 1976).

the most southerly representative of the Mull dyke swarm, was intruded into the country rock.

Apart from the exposures in the banks of the Tees and Greta, the southern part of County Durham has few good continuous sections. This is due to a variably thick covering of glacial deposits left by the most recent, late Devensian, ice advance. Resistant rock types form features in the landscape that rarely project through this mantle of **drift.**

EXCURSION DETAILS

Locality 1, Butterknowle (NZ 115255). Park on the B6282 at the south side of the bridge, then follow the track along the River Guanless downstream to where it bends sharply to the north. Continue straight on into the linear quarry which worked the Cleveland Dyke, here 10 m wide, for roadstone. Note the method of quarrying whereby 0.5 m of the dyke rock was left as a retaining wall on each side to prevent the collapse of the Westphalian country rock into the workings. Where the retaining wall has fallen away, weak contact **metamorphism** can be seen, the effect most pronounced in fine-grained lithologies. The dyke is a **porphyritic** tholeiitic dolerite with a microcrystalline groundmass and plagioclase **feldspar phenocrysts**; vesicles are also present. It is a typically massive, hard, dark grey to bluish-grey rock when fresh, but tends to darken when weathered and is easily distinguished from the country rock. The pattern of **joints** is rather irregular but appears to be sub-horizontal columnar jointing at the quarry face (NZ 118253).

On Cockfield Fell (NZ 122251) the dyke is 22 m wide, but entry to the workings is not possible there.

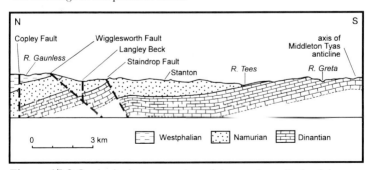

Figure 17.2 Geological cross-section of the northern limb of the Middleton Tyas anticline. Line of section on Fig. 17.1.

Locality 2 (NZ 131251–118255). From the quarry by the River Guanless, cross rough ground to the south to the dismantled Bishop Auckland to Tebay railway, which crosses Cockfield Fell, and follow its course eastwards until it crosses the river. Upstream along the south bank, several exposures of Westphalian sediments, between the Brockwell and Busty coal seams, can be seen. There is evidence of past coal mining activity, with many spoil heaps, and on the opposite bank, a dismantled railway (West Auckland to Butterknowle) which served the mines of the area. These mines were worked by pillar and stall. The coal in the pillars is now being removed by opencast mining throughout the area. Siltstones overlying a ripple cross-bedded sandstone crop out at NZ 126253, a cross-bedded sandstone at NZ 121255, and shales dipping 5° to the northwest at NZ 118255.

Return to the vehicle, drive south through Cockfield and take the A688 via Staindrop to Barnard Castle.

Locality 3, Barnard Castle (NZ 053159–048165). There is ample free car parking on the Demesnes (NZ 052161), on the north bank of the River Tees. From the footpath on the south bank, reach the riverside near the mill where a traverse through Yoredale cycles of the early Namurian can be examined (Fig. 17.3). The waterfall at the mill is formed by the dark-grey, thin-beddded, fine-grained Bottom Little

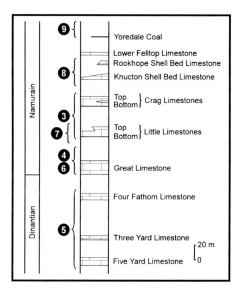

Figure 17.3 Succession of Carboniferous Limestone cyclothems between Barnard Castle and Piercebridge, indicating sections exposed at each locality.

Limestone (2.5 m) dipping 10° north. The 9 m shale with limestone ribs between the Bottom and Top Little Limestones is exposed between Demesnes and Thorngate Mills. Cross the footbridge to where the Top Little Limestone (5 m) can be seen on the north bank upstream of Thorngate Wynd (NZ 048161) forming a natural ledge across the River Tees. The overlying shale (6 m), which is poorly exposed, is capped by the Ten Fathom Grit (9 m) and can be seen under the County Bridge. This is succeeded by the Bottom (11 m) and Top (7 m) Crag Limestones with intervening shales; the castle stands on this sequence.

Return to the vehicle and from the market cross in Barnard Castle, take the minor road towards Whorlton, turning off to Egglestone Abbey.

Locality 4, Egglestone Abbey (NZ 066149). Park just before the Abbey Bridge under which the River Tees has cut a gorge in the grey, massively bedded, **bioclastic** Great Limestone which marks the base of the Namurian. Upstream, the soft overlying beds are covered until, on the northern side and set back from the river bank, the White Hazle Sandstone forms a cliff. The overlying Bottom Little Limestone is not seen. The siltstones, shales and thin Coal Sills sandstones between the Great Limestone and the White Hazle Sandstone are exposed further upstream in the northern bank of the river.

Drive onto the A66, turn left then first right to Greta Bridge.

Locality 5, Greta Bridge and Brignall (NZ 076119–086132). There is parking between the bridge and the Morritt Arms. Follow the River Greta upstream on the west bank to an exposure of the Five Yard Limestone (NZ 076119), the lowest limestone seen in the western half of the Middleton Tyas Anticline. It is a grey, fine-grained, bioclastic limestone with a fauna of **crinoid** stems, **corals** and **brachiopods**, gently dipping to the north. It forms a pavement at the river edge with the characteristic blocky pattern of the well-jointed Carboniferous limestones. Further downstream a brown, medium-grained, **limonitic** sandstone between the Five Yard and overlying Three Yard Limestones (NZ 078124) is exposed in a river cliff. Return to the footpath and continue to the Scotchman's Stone (NZ 081125), where the blue-grey, fine-grained, crinoidal Three Yard Limestone is exposed (better seen on the eastern bank). The Scotchman's Stone is a joint block of a brown, thick bedded, coarse-grained sandstone that has broken away from the cliff section seen above the eastern bank. It is seen again on the opposite bank at NZ 085128. The top of this sandstone is approximately 8 m below the base of the Four Fathom Limestone which is not exposed. From the bridge looking north, the high ground is formed by the outcrop of the Great Limestone, which is seen in the next locality.

Return across the A66 to the 'Meeting of the Waters'.

Locality 6, 'Meeting of the Waters' (NZ 085145). The metalled road to this locality is private but may be used as a footpath. Approaching the confluence with the River Tees, the River Greta has cut through the top 20 m of the east–west striking Great Limestone, and is generally flowing down the gentle northerly dip slope into the River Tees.

Return to the A66, turn left and take the first left to Whorlton.

Locality 7, Whorlton Lido (NZ 108145–113145). This is private property and a charge is made during the summer months for use of facilities and parking. However, there is a right of way through the property following the River Tees downstream to Wycliffe. Here the Tees flows over two small waterfalls formed by the resistant dark grey bioclastic Top Little Limestone. This 4 m thick unit dips 6° north, and is made up of three limestones, separated by grey shales that contain brachiopods. Overlying the Top Little Limestone are beds of fossiliferous shale and sandstone, which can be seen in the north bank and in Whorlton Beck.

Continue through Whorlton and take the A67 to Winston.

Locality 8, Winston Bridge (NZ 138158–143163). There is ample car parking by the roadside, on each side of the bridge. Take the footpath upstream on the south side to the river bank, then continue upstream with care along the water's edge to a small waterfall, formed by the 10 m thick, grey, fine-grained, thin bedded Knucton Shell Bed Limestone. This unit is full of well preserved brachiopods, principally *Spirifer*. Turn back towards the bridge to work up the easterly dipping succession. Note 5 m of fossiliferous shales with fine-grained sandstone ribs overlying the shell bed, succeeded by 6 m of medium-grained ferruginous sandstone. This sandstone dips into the river under the bridge, and with care can be viewed on the north bank upstream of the bridge. Above the path between the road and the southern river bank just downstream of the bridge, it is possible with care to view the overlying grey, fine to medium-grained, Rookhope Shell Bed Limestone. There is a brachiopod-rich block of the limestone beside the footpath.

Continue east on the A67 to a lay-by on the right at Gainford Spa.

Locality 9, Gainford Spa (NZ 162173). From the lay-by, take the footpath to the river. Adjacent to the spa is an exposure of yellow to brown-weathered, medium-grained, laminated Namurian sandstone, with abundant carbonaceous laminae at the base. The upper unit truncates the underlying unit, approximately 1 m above the footpath. This sandstone lies between the Lower and Upper Felltop Limestone and directly above the Yoredale Coal.

Continue east on the A67 to Piercebridge.

Locality 10, Piercebridge (NZ 21001545). Park in the village (can be difficult) and walk to a gap in the wall at the southwest end of the bridge. Through the gap, take the slippery steep 'path' to the riverside and walk c.70 m upstream to a vertical cliff. The gently dipping rock exposed here is near the base of the late Permian Raisby Formation and just above the unconformity on the Carboniferous. The unconformity crops out to the west but is unexposed. The Raisby Formation comprises buff slightly **calcitic** dolostone that is mainly vaguely thin- to medium-bedded but is divided into 1–1.5 m major units by notch-forming thin beds of brown leathery clay. The rock is very finely crystalline and microporous and much of it has been fragmented by internal mineralogical changes ('**autobrecciation**'). Poorly-preserved moulds of brachiopods, **bivalves**, **ostracodes** and **foraminifera** are present in some beds.

Continue east on the A67 to High Coniscliffe.

Locality 11, old quarry at High Coniscliffe (NZ 22511525). There is limited parking at the entry gate (NZ 22531530) on the A67 near the church. The enigmatic section in the main face is in lagoonal beds of the Ford Formation and comprises two rock units that meet at a sharp sub-horizontal very uneven surface (relief c.2 m). The lower unit (up to 3.5 m thick) is of soft, porous, finely oolitic buff dolostone in regular beds mainly 0.1–0.3 m thick, of which some are planar cross-bedded; the upper unit (up to 5 m) is generally massive finely crystalline pale grey hard limestone that bears faint hints of bedding (and ?cross-bedding) in a few patches. The massive unit has a reef-like appearance and it may be a lagoonal patch-reef, but samples of it have so far failed to reveal a diagnostic reef fauna. The limestone may be secondary ('dedolomite') and produced by the reaction between former dolostone and groundwater rich in dissolved calcium sulphate. Dome-shaped structures up to about 1.2 m across in a minor north face could be **algal**.

Geology in Northumbrian Museums

Steve Mclean *Hancock Museum, Newcastle upon Tyne*

INTRODUCTION

The museums listed in this guide are situated within the counties of Northumberland, Durham, Tyne and Wear, and Cleveland north of the River Tees. Local museums with geological collections or displays present an ideal starting point from which to investigate the geology of the immediate area. Such institutions tend to collect locally or regionally and often possess top quality specimens acquired over a long period of time, many from localities which are no longer accessible. This is particularly true considering the extensive mining history of the area and the quantity of specimens which have found their way into museums as a direct result. In addition, extensive U.K. or indeed world collections are not uncommon, usually resulting from the prodigious efforts of 19th century collectors during the 'Golden Age' of geology.

In the area represented by this guide, there are three principal geological collections housed in museums. By far the largest is the collection owned by the Natural History Society of Northumbria at the Hancock Museum in Newcastle (currently managed by Tyne and Wear Museums). The earliest part of this collection dates from the beginning of the 19th century and now contains approximately 50 000 specimens, the largest proportion of which are local Carboniferous and Permian fossils. There are over 8000 mineral specimens, principally from the North Pennine Orefield.

The second largest collection, located at Sunderland Museum, is owned by Tyne and Wear Museums. Although the oldest recorded specimen dates back to 1815, the rest of the collection was begun in 1836 when the Sunderland Natural History and Antiquarian Society was founded. There are approximately 20 000 geological specimens, the largest part consisting of Permian fossils and rocks from the

Zechstein strata of northeast England. The mineral collection contains over 4000 specimens collected principally from the North Pennine Orefield.

The third largest collection in the area is owned by Cleveland County Council and is housed at the Southlands Centre in Middlesbrough. The geological collection dates from 1975 and currently numbers 12–15 000 specimens, including minerals from northern England, especially the north Pennines, the Lake District and Caldbeck Fells, and regional Carboniferous, Permian and Jurassic fossils.

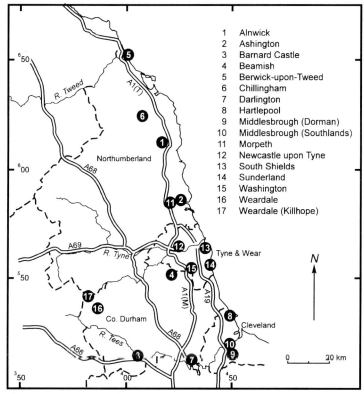

1 Alnwick
2 Ashington
3 Barnard Castle
4 Beamish
5 Berwick-upon-Tweed
6 Chillingham
7 Darlington
8 Hartlepool
9 Middlesbrough (Dorman)
10 Middlesbrough (Southlands)
11 Morpeth
12 Newcastle upon Tyne
13 South Shields
14 Sunderland
15 Washington
16 Weardale
17 Weardale (Killhope)

Figure 18 Location of museums of geological interest in Northumbria.

Key to museum listings

D Displays: L = Local; R(#) = Regional (# = C Cleveland, Y Yorkshire, NE Northern England [generally Northumberland, Tyne and Wear, Co. Durham, Cumbria]); **G** = General Geology.

TE Temporary Exhibitions, ask museum for details.

COL Collections: L = Local; R(#) = Regional (# = C,Y,NE as above); N = UK; WW = World Wide; m,r,f = minerals, rocks, fossils (M,R,F = particular strength); P = Photographic records, A = Archive, Li = geological library. Appointments should be made to examine collections, libraries, etc.

CAT Catalogues: Published catalogues of collections, histories of the collections etc., which may be available for purchase.

ENQ Enquiry Service: * = professional geologist on staff.

GACT Geological activities: Ask museum for details.

S Sales: Geological publications for sale.

AC Admission charge.

OPEN general opening hours. It is always best to check before you visit.

Where one or more of the above is not listed it is not relevant to a particular museum.

MUSEUMS

1. ALNWICK: Museum of Antiquities, Alnwick Castle, *Alnwick, Northumberland, NE66 1NQ, Tel. (01665) 510 777.* **COL** WW,R,M,Li; **AC** Yes; **OPEN** April–end Sept all week.

2. ASHINGTON: Woodhorn Colliery Museum, *Queen Elizabeth II Country Park, Ashington, Northumberland, Tel: (01670) 856968.* **D** (social and industrial history of mining and mining communities in southeast Northumberland, working winding engine); **AC** No; **OPEN** Wed.–Sun. all year.

3. BARNARD CASTLE: The Bowes Museum, *Barnard Castle, Co. Durham, DL12 8NP. Tel. (01833) 690606.* **COL** R(NE),N,WW,m,r,f (Carboniferous plants and rocks; minerals and rocks from around the world); **AC** Yes; **OPEN** all week, all year.

4. BEAMISH: The North of England Open Air Museum, *Beamish, Co. Durham, DH9 0RG, Tel. (01207) 231811.* **D** Social history of Coal

Mining, reconstructed pre-WWI coal mine; **COL** P,A,Li (relating to lead, coal and ironstone mining in North East England); **CAT** access to catalogues of P,A,Li collections by appointment; **S** mining; **AC** Yes; **OPEN** summer all week, winter closed Mon., Tues., Fri., (archive, library and mine closed during winter).

5. BERWICK: Berwick-upon-Tweed Borough Museum and Art Gallery, *The Clock Block, Berwick Barracks, Ravensdowne, Berwick-upon-Tweed, Northumberland, TD15 1DQ. Tel. (01289) 330044 ext. 253.* **COL** L,N,m,r,f,Li; **ENQ**; **AC** Yes; **OPEN** Easter–30th Sept, all week; 1st Oct–Easter, Tues–Sat.

6. CHILLINGHAM: Chillingham Castle, *Chillingham, Northumberland, NE66 5NJ, Tel. (01668) 215359.* **D** L (very small, Carboniferous plants); **TE**; **COL** L,f (Carboniferous plants, very small); **AC** Yes; **OPEN** May 1st–Oct 1st, all week except Tuesdays.

7. DARLINGTON: Darlington Museum, *Tubwell Row, Darlington, Co. Durham, DL1 1PD. Tel. (01325) 463795.* **D** R(NE) (rocks, minerals and fossils of the North East); **COL** N, WW,M,r,f; **ENQ**; **S** common specimens; **AC** No; **OPEN** All year, Mon–Sat (except Thursday afternoon), closed 1–2 pm.

8. HARTLEPOOL: Gray Art Gallery and Museum, *Clarence Road, Hartlepool, Cleveland, TS24 8BT, Tel. (01429) 268916 ext. 2610.* **D** L (geology of the Hartlepool area); **TE**; **COL** R(NE), WW(small),r,f,m,Li; **GACT** occasional; **OPEN** all week, all year (Sunday afternoon only).

9. MIDDLESBROUGH: Dorman Museum, *Linthorpe Road, Middlesbrough, Cleveland, Tel. (01642) 813781.* **D** (planned for the future); **TE**; **COL** R(C,Y),N,WW,m,r,F,A,Li; **CAT** catalogue information available for some parts of the collection; **ENQ** basic; **GACT** occasional; **S**; **AC** No; **OPEN** all year, Tues–Sat.

10. MIDDLESBROUGH: Southlands Centre, *Geology and Environmental Resource Section, Cleveland County Libraries and Leisure Dept., Ormesby Road, Middlesbrough, Cleveland, TS3 0YZ, Tel. (01642) 327583 ext. 220.* **COL** L,R(C,NE),N,WW,M,r,f, (see above) P,A,Li; **CAT** unpublished catalogues can be made available; **ENQ***; **AC** No; **OPEN** all year, Mon–Fri. Study and laboratory facilities available.

11. MORPETH: Wallington Hall *(National Trust)*, *Cambo, Near Morpeth, Northumberland, Tel. (01670) 774283*. **D** G (curiosity collection of rocks, minerals and fossils); **COL** L,N (small), m,R,f; **CAT** available to view in building; **AC** Yes; **OPEN** April 1st–Oct 31st all week, except Tuesday.

12. NEWCASTLE: Hancock Museum, *Barras Bridge, Newcastle upon Tyne, Tyne and Wear, NE2 4PT, Tel. (0191) 222 7418*. **D** L,R(NE),G; **TE**; **COL** L,R(NE),N,WW,M,r,F(see above),P,A,Li; **CAT** Yes, other collection information can be made available; **ENQ***; **GACT**; **S**; **AC** Yes; **OPEN** all week, all year (except Sunday mornings).

13. SOUTH SHIELDS: South Shields Museum and Art Gallery, *Ocean Road, South Shieds, Tyne and Wear, NE33 2TA, Tel. (0191) 456 8740*. **D** L (geology displays within local history context), **ENQ: GACT: S: AC** No; **OPEN** Tues–Sat, Sun pm, all year.

14. SUNDERLAND: Sunderland Museum and Art Gallery, *Borough Road, Sunderland, Tyne and Wear, SR1 1PP, Tel. (0191) 514 1235*. **D** L,R(C,NE); **TE**; **COL** L,R(NE),N,WW,M,r,F(see above); P,A,Li **CAT** No, but collection information available; **ENQ***; **GACT: S: AC** No; **OPEN** Tues–Sat, Sun pm, all year.

15. WASHINGTON: Washington 'F' Pit Museum, *Albany Way, Albany, Washington, Tyne and Wear, NE37 1BJ, Tel. (0191) 416 7640*. **D** L (Restored colliery winding engine house with working engine); **AC** No; **OPEN** April–Oct, Tues–Sat, Sun pm.

16. WEARDALE: The Weardale Museum, *Ireshopeburn, Weardale, Co. Durham, Tel. (01388) 537417*. **D** L (minerals and fossils, small); **TE**; **COL** L,M,f,P,Li(small); **AC** Yes; **OPEN** May, June, July, Sept, (Wed, Thurs, Sat & Sun); Aug every day.

17. WEARDALE: Killhope Lead Mining Centre, *Cowshill, Upper Weardale, Co. Durham, DL13 1AR. Tel.(01388) 537505*. **D** L,R(North Pennines), restored 19th century lead mining site with waterwheel); **TE; COL** R(North Pennines, collections relating to the industrial history of lead mining); **ENQ: GACT: S** (including souvenir specimens); **AC** Yes; **OPEN** April 1st–Oct 31st all week, Sun in November only.

FURTHER INFORMATION

Davis, P. and Brewer, C., 1986 *A Catalogue of Natural Science Collections in North-East England*. North of England Museums Service. Detailed local information regarding geological collections.

Nudds, J. (ed.), 1994 *Directory of British Geological Museums*. Geol. Soc. Misc. Papers, no. 18. Includes information on local museums.

Events in Tyne and Wear Museums are listed in a leaflet *Out and About in Tyne and Wear*.

Acknowledgements

Many thanks are due to all the institutions in this guide for providing the above information and particularly to Ken Sedman (Cleveland Geology and Environmental Resources), Tim Pettigrew and Alec Coles (Tyne and Wear Museums), and Andy Newman (University of Newcastle upon Tyne).

Glossary

Words in **_bold italic_** are defined elsewhere in the glossary.

accretionary prism   Wedge of material built up by underthrusting of successive slices of sediment on the landward side of a **_subduction_** zone.

acritarch   Marine, hollow, organic walled microfossil of uncertain affinities.

adit   More or less horizontal tunnel to mine.

agglomerate   **_Conglomerate_** or **_breccia_** of volcanic origin.

aggradation   Accumulation of sediment resulting in raising of the substrate.

alga   (pl. algae) Primitive plant-like organism. Some may secrete calcium carbonate and algal mats may play a role in sediment accumulation in some environments. *See* **_stromatolite._**

amygdale   Cavity within a lava, **_dyke_** or **_sill_**, lined or filled with secondary minerals.

andesite   Fine-grained volcanic rock of intermediate composition (with about 53–60% silica).

anhydrite $CaSO_4$ White to grey, rock-forming **_evaporite_** mineral.

ankerite $Ca(Fe,Mg,Mn)(CO_3)_2$ Mineral, may be crystalline of various colours but often yellowish-brown, massive or granular, commonly replacing the wallrock of Pennine veins.

anticline   *See* **_fold._**

apatite   Fluophosphate or chlorophosphate of calcium. Characteristically green or grey-green mineral in hexagonal prisms. Found in **_igneous_** and **_metamorphic_** rocks, and principal mineral of fossil bone.

aplite   Pinkish, fine-grained **_quartz_**-alkali **_feldspar_** rock associated with granite and usually occurring in **_veins._**

arenite   Sedimentary rock of sand-grade with <15% mud matrix (hence **arenaceous**).

argillaceous   Silt to clay grade sediments (grains <0.0625 mm diameter).

arkose   Sand-grade rock containing 25% or more **_feldspar._**

autobreccia   Rock broken into angular fragments by internal processes. Usually applied to a lava crust brecciated by continuing movement within the flow hence **autobrecciation**.

back-arc basin   Sedimentary basin formed behind a volcanic island arc, above a **_subduction_** zone.

baryte/barytes $BaSO_4$ **Baryte** is a colourless to white mineral, commonly in tabular crystals, noticeably heavy. A common **_gangue_** mineral. **Barytes** is the commercial product.

196

basalt Dark, often almost black, fine-grained basic volcanic rock, low in silica (no *quartz*) and relatively rich in iron, magnesium and calcium.

bioclast A shell or skeletal fragment.

biomicrite A *micritic* (mud-grade) limestone containing *bioclasts*.

biostrome Sheet-like accumulation of fossil shells or skeletons.

biotite Common, dark brown to black, Mg, Fe-rich *mica.*

bioturbation Reworking of unconsolidated sediment by burrowing organisms which may partly or completely destroy primary structures (i.e. bedding); hence **bioturbated.**

bismuthinite Bi_2S_3 Soft, greyish-white mineral, commonly in bladed crystals.

bivalve Marine to fresh-water *mollusc* in which the plane of symmetry of the bi-valved calcium carbonate shell is the plane of opening of the two valves (as in cockles or mussels).

Bouma sequence Idealized sequence of sedimentary structures found within a *turbidite* bed, from base: massive or graded sand; lower parallel lamination; ripple lamination; upper parallel lamination; pelagic shale.

B.P. Years before present (conventionally taken to be 1950).

brachiopod Solitary marine animal with bi-valved calcite shell. The plane of symmetry is perpendicular to the plane of opening of the valves.

breccia Coarse clastic rock in which the *clasts* are angular. *See also* *fault.*

bryozoa Small colonial animals with a calcite skeleton consisting of large numbers of tiny tubular or box-like chambers. Colonial form very variable.

calcite $CaCO_3$ Colourless or white mineral which is the main constituent of limestone. Crystals when formed (i.e. in *veins*) may be tabular or prismatic.

calcrete Nodular or massive, laminar carbonate bed formed in a soil in semi-arid regions.

Caledonian Mountains/Orogeny See *orogeny.*

carbonate rocks Limestones or *dolostones* (dolomites).

cassiterite SnO_2 Hard, heavy, usually reddish-brown to black mineral, massive or with pyramidal or prismatic crystals. In Northumbria, known only as minute inclusions in other vein minerals.

cataclastic Formed by shearing and granulation as a result of *tectonic* movement.

cementstone General term for extremely hard carbonate-rich bed capable of being ground as cement.

chalcedony SiO_2 White or greyish-white, fibrous to cryptocrystalline, stalactitic or botryoidal *quartz.*

chalcopyrite $CuFeS_2$ (copper pyrites) Brass-yellow mineral commonly with an iridescent tarnish. Most common copper mineral. Crystals usually tetrahedra.

197

chert Nodules, lenses or impersistent bands of cryptocrystalline *quartz*, usually black, grey or red in colour, usually of diagenetic origin in sedimentary sequences.

chlorite $(Mg,Fe)_5Al(AlSi_3)O_{10}$ Soft, green, platy mineral associated with low-grade *metamorphism*. Found also in *amygdales* and *veins*.

chute A downslope, sub-glacial *meltwater channel.*

clast Rock fragment; hence **clastic rock**. The principal clastic rocks are distinguished on grain size thus: *conglomerate* > 2 mm > sandstone > 0.0625 mm siltstones > 0.004 mm>mudstone/shale.

cleavage A close-spaced, regular fracture or fabric imposed on strongly *folded* beds and best developed in weaker, fine-grained rocks. Perfect cleavage is parallel to the axial plane of a fold.

cone-in-cone Fabric of adjacent sets of vertically nested cones, each about 3 cm or more in diameter, caused by precipitation of $CaCO_3$ under pressure in a mud-grade rock.

concretion Spherical or ellipsoidal, more resistant mass formed by local early cementation of the sediment. They often occur regularly or irregularly spaced in layers and weather out of the softer surrounding sediment.

conformable Sequence of rocks in apparently continuous succession.

conglomerate Coarse *clastic rock* in which the clasts are rounded. An **intraformational conglomerate** is one formed of locally derived clasts from a recently deposited source.

coral A polyp or polyps (anemone-like) with a basal skeleton of calcium carbonate. Corals may be solitary or colonial, the latter varying from flat, tabular masses to clusters of branching tubes.

crevasse Breach in a river bank or levee through which sediment-charged water may flow to form a **crevasse-splay** deposit.

crinoid (sea lily; feather star) Marine organism (echinoderm) with a plated cup, showing radio-pentameral symmetry and bearing feeding arms, supported in sea lilies by a stalk. The disc-shaped ossicles or columnals of the stalk are a major constituent of Palaeozoic limestones, hence crinoidal limestone.

cross-stratification, cross-bedding, cross-lamination Sedimentary structure in which the migration of the slip face of **ripples**, dunes or bars produces a series of inclined laminae (**foresets**) between sub-horizontal bedding surfaces. Different types are **planar**, when the laminae are flat, **trough**, when the laminae are scoop-shaped and **hummocky**, when individual **sets** of cross-beds cut across each other leaving hummocky bounding surfaces.

cyclothem A particular sequence of beds repeated again and again in vertical succession. Particularly notable in the Carboniferous (see *Yoredale*).

dacite Light-coloured, fine grained, volcanic rock of acid–intermediate composition.

deflation Erosion of land surfaces through the agency of wind.

diagenesis   The changes that take place in the conversion of a sediment to a rock.

diopside $CaMgSi_2O_6$ Pale, dirty green or grey silicate mineral of the *pyroxene* group, common in more basic igneous rocks. May form short prismatic crystals.

dip   The maximum angle of inclination of a planar surface, usually bedding. Measured in the vertical plane at right angles to the *strike.*

dolerite   Dark coloured, medium-grained igneous rock of *basaltic* composition.

dolomite $CaMg(CO_3)_2$ White, colourless, yellowish or brown mineral; rhombic crystals with curved faces. Term also used for the characteristically browny-yellow rock composed mainly of the mineral, but more correctly termed **dolostone**.

downthrow   *See* **throw.**

draa   A large sand ridge or dune chain, the largest desert landform.

drift   Any superficial, unconsolidated sediments of the Quaternary.

drumlin   Smooth, streamlined, oval mound of *till* (boulder clay), usually in groups (drumlin field or swarm), formed beneath an advancing ice sheet. The long axis of the drumlin is parallel to the direction of advance.

dyke   More or less vertical, cross-cutting intrusion. May exist **en echelon**, as discrete, overlapping or more distant, offset elements (**echelons**).

echelon   See *dyke.*

echinoid   (sea urchin) Marine invertebrate with body enclosed in a globular or discoidal test. Symmetry either pentameral radial (regular echinoids) or pentameral bilateral (irregular, burrowing, echinoids).

epidote $Ca_2(Al,Fe)_3(SiO_4)_2OH$ Characteristically green, radial, fibrous or columnar mineral, sometimes forming prismatic crystals, associated with *hydrothermal* or contact *metamorphic* rocks.

erratic   Glacially transported rock derived from outside the local area.

esker   Long, sinuous, steep-sided ridge consisting of sands and gravels, formed either in an englacial tunnel or at the edge of a retreating ice sheet.

eustatic   World-wide change in sea level.

euxinic   Environment with little or no oxygen, and sediments formed therein.

evaporite   Rocks or minerals formed by precipitation of salts from natural brines by evaporation.

facies   Features of a rock or rock sequence that reflect the environment of deposition.

facing   Direction in which beds in a *fold* hinge become younger.

fault   A more or less planar fracture in a rock mass along which relative displacement of adjacent blocks has occurred. The face of the block above an inclined fault plane is the **hanging wall**, that below is the **footwall**. In most faults, the direction of movement is known or assumed to be predominantly vertical. In a **strike-slip** or **wrench** fault, the direction of movement on a sub-vertical plane is predominantly horizontal. A **thrust** fault has a sub-horizontal plane of displacement. Fractured rock on the fault plane caused by movement between adjacent blocks is a fault *breccia.*

feldspars   Important group of rock-forming silicate minerals, common in **igneous** rocks, hence **feldspathic. Alkali feldspar** is K– Na series feldspar. **Plagioclase** is Na–Ca series feldspar, often forming white, lath-shaped *phenocrysts* in igneous rocks. Most feldspars break down quickly on weathering.

fireclay   *See seatearth.*

flat   A lenticular zone of mineralization parallel to bedding.

flaser bedding   Ripple bedding with silt or clay drapes between sets.

fluorite CaF_2 Colourless to translucent, purple, green or yellow mineral commonly crystallising in cubes. **Fluorspar** is the commercial product.

flute cast (flute mark)   *See sole structure.*

fold   A bend in bedded rocks or any planar rock mass. An **anticline** is arched upwards with older rocks in the core. A **pericline** is an anticline in the form of an elongated dome. A **syncline** is bent downwards with younger rocks in the core. A **monocline** is a step-shaped fold, with one steep limb between two hinges. An **isoclinal fold** has subparallel fold limbs. The dip of the fold axis is the **plunge** of the fold.

foraminifera   Microscopic single-celled organism with a chambered, usually calcium carbonate, test.

foresets   *See cross-stratification.*

galena PbS Lead grey mineral crystallizing in cubes and octahedra. The main ore of lead.

gangue   Non-metallic mineral (i.e. *quartz, fluorite, baryte*) in *veins* with which ore minerals are associated. Formerly of no commercial value, fluorite and baryte are now important products.

ganister   *See seatearth.*

garnet   Group of Ca, Fe, Mg, Mn silicate minerals of variable composition, often deep reddish-brown in colour, found in *igneous* and *metamorphic* rocks.

gastropod   *Mollusc* with a usually helically coiled calcium carbonate shell (snail) or naked (slug).

glacioeustatic   *Eustatic* changes in sea level resulting from growth or decay of an ice sheet.

glaciofluvial   Sediments or landforms produced by meltwater from a glacier.

glaciogenic   Of glacial origin.

gley   Waterlogged, anaerobic soil.

gneiss   Coarse-grained, banded rock formed under high-grade *metamorphic* conditions.

graben A linear tract of country, lowered between two bounding *faults*. A **half-graben** is fault-bounded on one side only.

graptolite Extinct group of marine, *pelagic*, colonial organisms with an organic skeleton. Individuals a few mm long, colonies 10's mm long. Usually preserved as a carbonaceous film.

granite A coarse-grained acid igneous rock containing *quartz*, alkali *feldspar* and *mica.*

granodiorite A coarse-grained acid–intermediate *igneous* rock containing *quartz* and dominant plagioclase *feldspar.*

granophyre A granite characterized by fine-scale intergrowths of **quartz** and **feldspar**.

greywacke A poorly sorted (immature) silt-sand grade *clastic* rock with $>15\%$ clay-grade material.

gypsum $CaSO_4.2H_2O$ *Evaporite* mineral, usually white, finely granular or massive. A transparent variety (**selenite**) may be precipitated within sediments under some conditions. The fibrous form (satin spar) may form *veins.*

haematite Fe_2O_3 Steel-grey to black, sometimes red mineral, occurring as tabular crystals or massive, often botryoidal.

half-graben *See graben.*

halite (rock salt) NaCl Common salt, an evaporite mineral, usually white, crystals usually cubes.

hanging wall *See fault.*

hornblende Green or brown rock-forming silicate mineral of the amphibole group, characterised by two cleavages intersecting at $124°$.

hornfels Massive hardened, splintery rock formed by alteration of the country rock by contact (thermal) *metamorphism.*

hummocky cross-stratification *See cross-stratification.*

hush Opencast workings or trials excavated in part by releasing torrents of water from reservoirs high on a hillside. Large examples may be difficult to distinguish from natural valleys.

hydrothermal Associated with the action of hot water.

imbrication More or less parallel orientation of platy/tabular clasts, generally sloping up-current and thus indicating the direction of water flow.

igneous Rocks crystallized or solidified from a molten state. May be divided into **basic** (45–53% silica), **intermediate** (53–60% silica), and **acid** ($>$60% silica, including free **quartz**).

inlier Area of older rocks surrounded by younger rocks.

intermontane basin Sedimentary basin being infilled from erosion of surrounding mountains.

intraclast Fragment derived from the erosion of a nearby sediment and redeposited within the same area.

isoclinal See *fold.*

jarosite $KFe_3(SO_4)_2(OH)_6$ Yellowish-brown, usually earthy mineral of secondary origin.

joint   Fracture in rock along which little or no movement can be detected. Usually they occur in more or less regularly spaced sets, and two or more sets may intersect at various angles. As well as ***tectonic*** joints, they may form through cooling (***igneous*** rocks) or shrinkage in a sediment.

kame   Steep sided mound of bedded ***glaciofluvial*** sand and gravel associated with stagnant ice. A **kame terrace** is a continuous linear feature formed between an ice mass and a valley wall. Subsequent ice melt may result in signs of marginal slumping.

kettle hole   Depression in glacial ***drift***, possibly containing a lake, left by the melting of an included mass of ice.

laccolith   Concordant, lenticular, ***igneous*** intrusion, elliptical or circular in plan.

lacustrine   Sediment or processes associated with lakes.

lag   An accumulation of coarse ***clastic*** or ***bioclastic*** material, usually in the floor of a channel.

limonite   A general term for unspecified hydrous earthy iron oxides usually derived from the weathering of iron minerals in rocks or ***veins.***

linguoid   Tongue-shaped (of asymmetrical ripples).

lithology   Physical features of a rock. Hence **lithostratigraphy**, the statigraphic ordering of different rock types; **lithification,** process of turning unconsolidated sediment into rock.

Ma   Abbreviation for 'million years'.

magma   A hot, liquid or semi-liquid melt within the Earth's crust; the source for all ***igneous*** rocks and processes.

marcasite FeS_2 Pale brass-yellow or greyish metallic mineral, common as bladed or laminated crystalline masses in Pennine ***veins.***

marl   A calcareous clay with 35–65% soft calcium carbonate.

meltwater channel   Channel cut by the action of meltwater from a glacier or from snow. Usually unrelated to the present drainage pattern.

metamorphic   Rock formed by the alteration of a pre-existing rock by changes in temperature and/or pressure.

metasediment   A ***metamorphosed*** sediment.

mica   A group of complex silicate minerals characterised by a strongly platy habit.

micrite   Microcrystalline calcite (lime mud).

microgranite   A medium-grained (1–5 mm) rock of granitic composition.

mineral veins   *See* ***veins.***

mollusc   One of a very diverse invertebrate group including the ***bivalves***, ***gastropods***, and cephalopods (***nautiloids***, etc.)

monocline   See ***fold.***

moraine   An unsorted deposit of rock debris associated with the actions of a glacier.

nautiloid   Cephalopod ***mollusc*** with a curved or straight, tapering, chambered shell; ***suture*** simple, siphuncular tube central in chambers.

olivine   A group of olive green to brown or black rock-forming Mg, Fe silicate minerals, characteristic of silica-poor **igneous** rocks.

oncolite   Spherical or sub-spherical particle up to 50 mm diameter formed by the action of ***algae*** in trapping sediment on the surface of a mobile grain.

oolite   Rock formed largely of ***ooliths.*** Characteristic of high-energy, shallow-water environments.

oolith   Spherical or sub-spherical particle less than 2 mm diameter formed by the concentric deposition of rings of (usually) calcium carbonate around a mobile grain.

orogeny   Process of mountain building by the lateral compression of thick rock sequences. The **Caledonian Orogenic Cycle** refers to a series of orogenic events in the Lower Palaeozoic culminating in the late Silurian/early Devonian. The **Variscan Orogeny**, whose main effects are seen in southwest England and Central Europe, spanned the late Devonian to late Carboniferous.

ostracode   Small to microscopic, marine to fresh-water crustacean with calcitic bivalved shell.

outlier   Area of younger rocks surrounded by older rocks.

overflow channel, spillway Channel carved by the overflow from an ice-dammed lake. Usually unrelated to the present drainage pattern.

overstep   Relationship where a bed deposited by a ***transgression*** rests on the eroded ends of several beds below the plane of ***unconformity.***

palaeosol   Fossil soil.

pedogenic   Associated with soil formation.

pegmatite   Exceptionally coarse-grained variety of an ***igneous*** rock.

pelagic   Organisms living in the body of the water, either floating (planktonic) or swimming (nektonic).

pericline   See **fold.**

phenocryst Larger, usually well-formed crystal in a finer groundmass.

phonolite Fine grained, porphyritic, Na-rich volcanic rock.

phytoplankton   See ***plankton.***

plankton   Mainly small to microscopic organisms that float in near-surface oceanic waters; divided into **phytoplankton** (photosynthetic) and **zooplankton** (animals).

plate   A part of the Earth's rigid outer shell (lithosphere), internally relatively free of earthquakes and volcanic activity but bounded by more or less continuous zones of earthquakes and volcanoes where the plates move against each other. **Plate tectonics** describes the processes and effects of plate motions and interactions.

plunge   *See* **fold.**

pluton   A large ***igneous*** intrusion (excluding ***dykes*** and ***sills***).

porphyrite   Medium grained, intrusive ***igneous*** rock with many conspicuous feldspar ***phenocrysts***; hence **porphyritic** = containing phenocrysts.

Glossary

post   A bed of rock, often applied to limestones.

progradation   The outward extension of a sedimentary deposit, such as a delta building out from a shoreline.

pseudomorph   Retention of the original crystal form after a mineral has been replaced.

pyrite FeS_2 (fools gold) Common pale brass-yellow mineral, often crystallising in cubes.

pyroclastic   A *clastic* rock of volcanic origin.

pyroxene   Important group of dark green, brown or black, rock-forming silicate minerals, characterised by two cleavages at right-angles; crystals prismatic.

pyrrhotite   (magnetic pyrites) FeS Bronze-yellow, reddish-brown weathering, usually massive or granular mineral; magnetic.

quartz SiO_2 Very common mineral, usually transparent or white but may be variously coloured. Occurs in many *igneous* and *metamorphic* rocks, is the main constituent of sandstones and siltstones and a common *gangue* mineral in *veins* when prismatic crystals with a six-faced pyramidal termination may be found.

regression   Withdrawal of the sea from the land area due to a relative fall in sea level.

rhyolite   Fine-grained acid *igneous* extrusive rock; volcanic equivalent of granite.

rock-salt   *See **halite**.*

schist   A metamorphic rock with a strong, platy fabric, caused by the parallel alignment of *micas*.

seafloor spreading   Process whereby volcanic activity at mid-ocean ridges causes igneous rock material to be accreted to **plate** margins resulting in the growth of oceanic crust.

seatearth   A fossil soil with root traces found immediately below a coal seam. A **fireclay** is a pure clay seatearth, whilst a **ganister** is a pure quartz sand seatearth.

septarian   Nodules or *concretions* with a series of internal mineral-filled (usually *calcite*) cracks. Results from the formation of a hardened exterior shell before desiccation and shrinkage of the material inside the nodule.

serpulid   A group of polychaete worms with calcareous tubes.

sheath fold   A highly deformed fold form with a strongly curved fold axis, produced in shear zones.

siderite $FeCO_3$ Grey to grey-brown mineral widespread in certain sedimentary rocks, particularly sedimentary ironstone deposits and Coal Measures sequences. Also common in many Pennine *veins.*

siliciclastic   *Clastic* rocks formed predominantly of *quartz*, other silicate mineral and rock fragments.

sill   A tabular *igneous* intrusion, mainly concordant with bedding, although it may cut across beds from one level to another.

slickensides   A lineation on a *fault* or bedding plane caused by the relative movement of rock masses on either side. The surface is often coated by fibrous crystals, usually of *quartz* or *calcite*, aligned in the direction of movement.

sole mark/structure   Sedimentary structure cut into an underlying mud by a turbidity current and infilled by the overlying *turbidite* bed. Preserved as a cast on the base of the turbidite. **Flute cast (mark):** ovoid scoop-shaped structure caused by turbulent water flow, preserved as a tapered lobe on the base of the turbidite. Sole marks may also occur less typically in fluvial sediments, etc.

solifluction   Downhill movement of surface layer of unconsolidated weathered material when saturated by water.

sphalerite   (blende) ZnS Commonly a brown or black mineral with a resinous lustre and variable form. Most common ore of zinc.

spillway   1. General term for glacial *meltwater* or *overflow channels*. 2. Overflow channel constructed on a dam.

sponge   Primitive invertebrates with an asymmetrical body supported by spongin and/or siliceous or calcareous spicules. Some may have a massive calcareous basal skeleton.

S.S.S.I.   Site of Special Scientific Interest.

stadial   A period of increased cold or advancing ice.

stope   Underground excavation in a *vein.*

strike   Intersection of a bedding plane, or other planar surface, with the horizontal.

strike-slip   *See fault.*

stromatolite   A carbonate rock with a fine horizontal, domal or columnar banding, reflecting the control of deposition by an *algal* mat or microbial community living on the surface of the sediment.

stylolite   An irregular, suture like contact, most common in limestones, produced by solution of the rock under high pressure.

subduction   The process whereby oceanic crust descends into the interior of the Earth beneath oceanic or continental crust at a convergent *plate* margin.

suture   1. A linear zone of continental collision, marking the site of a former ocean. 2. Line of junction of septum with conch wall in cephalopods.

syncline   *See fold.*

tachylite   Black, glassy rock formed by chilling of a *basaltic* lava or shallow *igneous* intrusion.

tectonic   Relating to deformation of rock masses, as in mountain-building episodes.

tholeiitic basalt/dolerite   A type of *basalt/dolerite* oversaturated in silica, so that small amounts of *quartz* are present.

throw   Description of vertical component of movement on a *fault* plane. **Downthrow** emphasises the relative downward displacement of a block on one side of the fault, **upthrow** (less commonly used) emphasises the relative upward displacement of a block.

thrust   *See fault.*

till   (boulder clay) Collective term for the group of unsorted sediments laid down by direct action of ice.

tourmaline   A group of complex boro-silicate minerals, normally black or bluish-black; prismatic crystals with a typical triangular cross-section.

trace fossil   A structure resulting from the activity of an animal, such as a burrow or a grazing trail.

transgression   1. An advance of the sea over the land, caused by a relative rise in sea level. 2. Change of stratigraphic level by a *sill.*

tremolite $Ca_2(Mg,Fe)SiO_8O_{22}(OH)_2$ White or greyish-white mineral with needle-like crystals.

trilobite   Extinct group of arthropods, with a dorsal skeleton divided into head (cephalon), thorax and tailplate (pygidium).

tufa   Rock formed by the depositon of calcium carbonate (more rarely silica) as a sometime porous and/or banded mass around saline springs, or associated with stalactites and stalagmites.

tuff   Lithified volcanic ash-fall.

turbidite   Rock deposited from a **turbidity current/flow**, a fast flowing turbulent current charged with a high sediment load, commonly initiated by the disturbance of soft sediment on a slope. A turbidite is poorly sorted but may show grading and *sole structures* on its base.

unconformity   Surface of contact between two groups of rocks resulting from the tilting or folding and erosion of the lower group (often in an *orogenic* event) before the deposition of the upper group.

Variscan Orogeny   *See orogeny.*

vein/veinlet   A fracture, usually sub-vertical, which is mineralized, often with *quartz* or *calcite*. Crystals may grow from the walls towards the centre. A **mineral vein** normally implies the presence of ore minerals.

volcaniclastic   A *clastic* rock of volcanic origin.

witherite $BaCO_3$ A white, pale creamish white or grey mineral, crystals six-sided prisms and pyramids. Notably heavy.

xenolith   An inclusion of country rock within an *igneous* body.

Yoredale   Name applied to repeat cycles of limestone-shale-sandstone (-seatearth-coal) (*cyclothems*) in the Carboniferous (Dinantian, early Namurian), derived from the old name for Wensleydale, where they are typically developed.

Bibliography

General

Johnson, G. A. L. (compiler), in press. *The geology of North East England.*
Special publication, Natural History Society of Northumbria.
Newcastle upon Tyne.

Robson, D.A. (ed.). *The geology of North East England.* pp. iv+113.
Special publication, Natural History Society of Northumbria.
Newcastle upon Tyne.

Taylor, B. J., Burgess, I. C., Land, D. H., Mills, D. A. C., Smith, D. B.
& Warren, P. T. 1971. *Northern England.* British Regional Geology.
4th edn, pp. x+125. H.M.S.O., London.

Reference Works

Allaby, A. & Allaby, M. 1990. *The Concise Oxford Dictionary of Earth
Sciences.* xxi+410pp. O.U.P., Oxford.

British Museum (Natural History) 1975. *British Palaeozoic Fossils.* 4th
edn. 203pp. London.

Hamilton, W. R., Woolley, A. R. & Bishop, A. C. 1992. *Minerals, rocks
and fossils.* 320pp. Hamlyn, London.

Roberts, J.L. 1989. *Field guide to geological structures.* 250pp. Macmillan,
London.

Schumann, W. 1985 (1992). *Rocks, minerals and gemstones.* 380pp. Harper
Collins, London.

Specific

Only works quoted in the text are listed here. Further articles on various
aspects of the geology and geomorphology of Northumbria may be found
particularly in the *Proceedings of the Yorkshire Geological Society* as well as
many other journals, British Geological Survey Memoirs, and Geologists
Association guides.

Aspinall, R. J., Macklin, M. G. & Brewis, T. 1986. Metal mining and
floodplain sedimentation at Garrigill, and their influence on terrace
and floodplain soil development. *In* Macklin, M. G. & Rose, J,
(eds). *Quaternary river landforms and sediments in the northern Pennines:
field guide,* 35–45. British Geomorphological Research Group and
Quaternary Research Association.

Carruthers, R. G., Dinham, C. H., Burnett, G. A. & Maden, J. 1927.
The Geology of Belford, Holy Island, and the Farne Islands. *Memoir*

Bibliography

of the British Geological Survey, Sheet 4, pp. x+195. H.M.S.O., London.

Cope, J. C. W., Ingham, J. K. & Rawson, P. F. (eds) 1992. Atlas of palaeogeography and lithofacies. Geological Society Memoir No. 13, 153pp, 106 maps.

Day, J. B. W. 1970. Geology of the country around Bewcastle. *Memoir of the British Geological Survey*, Sheet 12 (England and Wales), pp. xi+357. H.M.S.O., London.

Dunham, K. C. 1990. Geology of the Northern Pennine Orefield, Volume 1. Tyne to Stainmore. 2nd edn., pp x+299. *Memoir of the British Geological Survey*, H.M.S.O., London.

Elliott, T. 1976. Sedimentary sequences from the Upper Limestone Group of Northumberland. *Scottish Journal of Geology*, **12**, 115–124.

Farmer, N. & Jones, J. M. 1969. The Carboniferous, Namurian rocks of the coast section from Howick Bay to Foxton Hall, Northumberland. *Transactions of the Natural History Society of Northumberland, Durham and Newcastle upon Tyne*, **17**, 1–27.

Frost, D. V. & Holliday, D. W. 1980. Geology of the country around Bellingham. *Memoir of the British Geological Survey*, Sheet 13, pp. x+112. H.M.S.O., London.

Fullerton, B. & Sharp, J. (Eds.) 1980. *Excursions in North-East England*. 102 pp. Department of Geography, University of Newcastle upon Tyne for the Geographical Association, Tyneside Branch.

Grieg, D. C. 1988. Geology of the Eyemouth district. *Memoir of the British Geological Survey*, Sheet 34 (Scotland), pp. viii+78. H.M.S.O., London.

Hollingworth, N. T. J. & Pettigrew, T. H. 1988. *Zechstein reef fossils and their palaeoecology*. Palaeontological Association Guides to Fossils, No. 3, pp. iv+75. London.

Hunt, C. J. 1984. *The lead miners of the northern Pennines in the eighteenth and nineteenth centuries*. 282pp. Davis, Newcastle upon Tyne.

Jhingran, A. G. 1943. The Cheviot Granite. *Quarterly Journal of the Geological Society of London*, **98**, 241–254.

Johnson, G. A. L. 1952. A glacial erratic boulder of Shap Granite in South Northumberland. *Geological Magazine* **89**, 361–364.

Johnson, G. A. L. 1959. The Carboniferous stratigraphy of the Roman Wall district in western Northumberland. *Proceedings of the Yorkshire Geological Society* **32**, 83–130.

Johnson, G. A. L. & Richardson, G. 1990. Coal Measures of the River Wear Gorge at Durham, England. *Transactions of the Natural History Society of Northumbria* vol.55, pt. 2, 84–96.

Lumsden, G. I., Tulloch, W., Howells, M. F. & Davies, A. 1967. The Geology of the neighbourhood of Langholm. *Memoir of the British Geological Survey*, Sheet 11 (Scotland), pp. viii+255. H.M.S.O., London.

Lunn, A. G. 1980. Quaternary. *In* Robson, D.A. (ed.). *The geology of North East England*, pp.48–60. Special Publication, Natural History Society of Northumbria. Newcastle upon Tyne.

McAdam, A. D., Clarkson, E. N. K. & Stone, P. 1992. *Scottish Borders geology: an excursion guide*. pp. x+220. Scottish Academic Press.

Mills, D. A. C. & Hull, J. H. 1976. Geology of the country around Barnard Castle. *Memoir of the British Geological Survey*, Sheet 32, pp. xii+385. H.M.S.O., London.

Raistrick, A. R. & Jennings, B. 1965. *A history of lead mining in the Pennines*. 347 pp. Longmans, London.

Randall, B. A. O. & Farmer, N. 1970. The Holy Island Dyke. *Transactions of the Natural History Society of Northumberland, Durham and Newcastle upon Tyne*, **17**, 79–91.

Reynolds, A. D. 1992. Storm, wave and tide-dominated sedimentation in the Dinantian Middle Limestone Group, Northumbrian Basin. *Proceedings of the Yorkshire Geological Society*, **49**, 135–148.

Scarboro, D. & Tucker, M. E. 1995. Amphibian footprints from the mid-Carboniferous of Northumberland, England. *Palaeoecology, Palaeoclimatology, Palaeogeography*, **113**, 335–349.

Scotese, C. R. & McKerrow, W. S. 1990. Revised World maps and introduction. *In* McKerrow, W. S. & Scotese, C. R. (eds) *Palaeozoic palaeogeography and biogeography*. Geological Society Memoir No. 12, 1–21.

Smith, D. B., 1994. *The geology of the Sunderland district*. Memoir of the British Geological Survey, Sheet 21, pp. xii+161. H.M.S.O., London.

Turnbull, L. 1975. *The history of lead mining in the north east of England*. 80pp. Harold Hill and Son, Newcastle upon Tyne.

Index

Index

Fisherman's Haven, 44
Five Yard Limestone, 130, 165, 187
Five Yard Limestone Cyclothem, 175, 178
Five-Quarter Coal, 101, 103
flagstone, 172, 176
Flandrian Stage, 138, 145
flat, 17, 155, 157, 158, 161
floodplain, 33, 145
flow-banded, 61
fluorite, 17, 155, 157, 160, 161, 165
fluorspar, 157, 158, 159
flute cast/mark, 37, 58
fluvial, 14, 16, 19, 27, 39, 84, 86
fluviatile, 23
fluvio-deltaic, 33, 50, 63
fluvio-lacustrine, 30, 39
foraminifera, 189
Force Garth Quarry, 180
Ford Formation, 148, 152, 183, 189
Ford Quarry, 148
Ford-Felkington Disturbance Zone, 78
Four Fathom Limestone, 131, 132, 133, 166, 176
Four Fathom Limestone Cyclothem, 176
Foxton Limestone, 84
Frazer's Hush Mine, 159
Frazer's Hush(es), 158, 159
Frosterley, 166
Frosterley Marble/Band, 160, 163, 166, 176

Gainford Spa, 189
galena, 17, 39, 116, 133, 155, 157, 158, 160, 161, 165
Galloway, 20
gangue, 17, 155
ganister, 45, 82, 90, 133, 175
garnet, 104
Garrigill, 143
gastropod, 45, 69, 86, 121, 152
'gastropods', vermiform, 15, 65, 67
Gigantoproductus, 47, 50, 178
Gilsland, 69
Gilsland Fault Belt, 69
glacial, 63, 92, 105, 110, 119, 163, 180
glacial deposit, 62, 185
glaciation, 20, 23, 34, 55, 73, 86, 102, 131, 138–145, 173, 180, 181
glacioeustatic, 147
glaciofluvial, 20, 138, 140
Glencartholm Volcanic Beds, 67
gley, 140
gneiss, 96
Gondwana, 18

granite, 14, 17, 30, 53, 55, 56, 57, 106, 158
granodiorite, 58
granophyre, 110
granophyric granite, 58
graptolite, 11, 22, 26
graptolitic, 33
gravel, 20, 23, 63, 138, 139, 173
Great Limestone, 16, 52, 132, 133, 135, 145, 155, 157, 160, 161, 163, 166, 176, 187, 188
Green Grove Sandstone, 69
Green's Haven (Bay), 44, 46, 47
Green's Haven Fault, 47
Greencleugh Mine, 158, 159
Greencleugh Vein, 159
Greta Bridge, 187
greywacke, 14, 21, 22, 23, 25, 31, 33, 35, 37, 39, 58, 106, 115, 125, 126
grit, 172
gritstone, feldspathic, 173
Groverake Mine, 158
Groverake Vein, 158
gypsum, 15, 39

haematite, 57
halite, 15, 19, 147
Hall, Sir James, 25
Haltwhistle, 133, 136
Haltwhistle Burn, 133–136
Harehope Quarry, 166
Harkess Rocks, 79
Harthope Burn, 56
Harthope Fault, 111
Hartlepool Anhydrite, 19, 99
Hartley Bay, 102
Hartside Pass, 138, 142
Hawick Group, 31, 33, 35, 37
Hawsen Burn, 56
Haydon Bridge, 138
head, 55
Henry Pit, 169
Heugh Hill, 74, 76
Hexham, 138
High Coniscliffe, 189
High Force, 179
High Grains Sandstone Member, 67
Holburn Anticline, 107
Holm Head Vein, 175
Holocene, 63
Holwick Head Bridge, 179
Holwick Scars, 181
Holy Island, 71, 73, 74–79
Holy Island Dyke, 73, 76
hornblende, 35
hornfelsed, 57
Horse Road Sandstone, 30
Howdiemont Bay, 84
Howick, 81–91
Howick Bay, 86, 88
Howick Burn, 85

Howick Fault, 86, 90
Howick Haven, 85
Howick Limestone, 85, 86, 87, 90
Hudeshope Beck, 175
Huds Head, 47, 49
Hudshouse, 124
Hudshouse Dyke, 125
hummocky cross-stratification, 50
hush, 161, 181
Hutton Coal, 99, 169
Hutton's Unconformity, 21, 115
Hutton, James, 25
hydrothermal, 53
hydrothermal alteration, 55, 57
hydrothermally altered, 57, 61

Iapetus Ocean, 11, 22, 33, 55, 106
Iapetus suture, 14, 55, 106
igneous, 34, 172
igneous activity, 19
imbricate, 111
imbrication, 26, 29, 35
intermontane basin, 14
intrusion, 17, 33, 34, 53, 70, 73, 115, 172
Inverclyde Group, 23
iron, 172, 178
iron ore, 157
iron oxide, 45, 46
Iron Scars Limestone, 85
ironstone, 30, 45, 46, 47, 73, 78, 93, 96, 101, 102, 112, 121, 132, 133, 175
Irthing Gorge, 69
Irthing Shell Bed, 69
isoclinal fold, 36

jarosite, 46
Jew Limestone, 128
Junction Limestone Member, 65

kame, 20
kame terrace, 20
kamiform, 138, 140
Kay Crag, 112
kettle hole, 20, 140
Kielder Dam, 119
Kielder Reservoir, 119
Killhope Burn, 160
Killhope Lead Mining Centre, 159
Kinderscoutian Stage, 84
Kinnesswood Formation, 23
Kirklington Sandstone, 63
Knucton Shell Bed Limestone, 188

laccolith, 55
lacustrine, 14, 27, 93

Index

215

Index